Helping Others Change

HOW GOD CAN USE YOU *to* HELP PEOPLE GROW

PARTICIPANT'S WORKBOOK—THIRD EDITION

Paul David Tripp

Timothy S. Lane, Contributor

1-800-318-2186
www.ccef.org

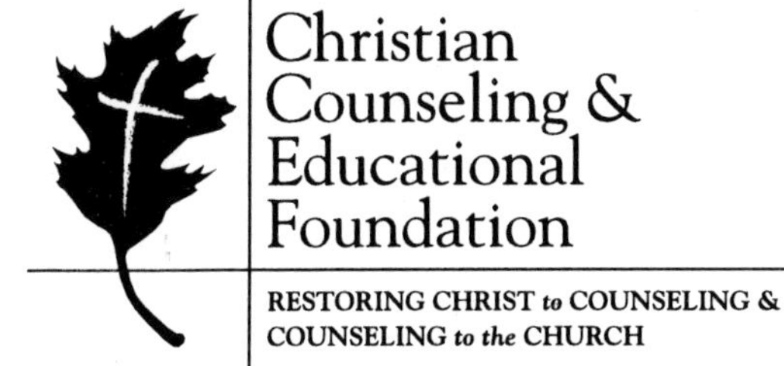

Helping Others Change
Workbook
Third Edition

Printed in Canada.

ISBN 978-0-9762308-8-5

ACKNOWLEDGMENTS

It would be impossible to acknowledge the host of people who have contributed to the content and development of this curriculum over the years. However, there are a few who must be mentioned. Thanks to Sue Lutz, whose editorial work has made this a much better training tool. Jayne Clark contributed her organizational skill and made a dream a doable project. Karen Barnard typed and retyped draft after draft until the job was done. We would also like to thank our publisher, Punch Press, for encouraging us through their support of this project. The faculty of CCEF encouraged and supported me throughout the design and writing of the curriculum, and contributed to its content. The entire staff of CCEF has touched this project in some way. Thanks to all of you.

We want to offer special thanks to all the churches around the country that were willing to test this course. You have encouraged us and sharpened the curriculum. Your work has been a very important step in creating the final product.

Our particular gratitude goes to the churches and individuals who gave sacrificially to support the development of this curriculum. This is the most costly and time-consuming project CCEF has ever done, and we could not have completed it without your help. Your partnership has not only enabled us to continue, but it has encouraged us along the way. On behalf of the churches around the world that will use this material and the myriad of people who will grow and change as a result, we say, "Thank you."

Few things in ministry have so clearly depicted to us what Paul says about the church in Ephesians 4:16: "From him the whole body, joined and held together by every supporting ligament, grows and builds itself up in love, as each part does its work."

A Word of Welcome

Welcome to ***Helping Others Change***. We are thankful for you and your desire to be effective for Christ. Our prayer is that this course will produce a wonderful harvest of lasting change in you and those you reach.

Perhaps a few words would be helpful about the course you are about to take.

1. Our goal in this course is to equip you for personal growth and ministry. What is here has been carefully and prayerfully included and then tested in churches throughout the country.

2. We use the word "counseling" throughout this course, but by no means do we limit its definition to the more formal, professional meaning. When the course talks about "counseling," it means "personal ministry." It's talking about getting alongside people to serve them—to assist them in making the changes God wants them to make. This kind of counseling is not just a formal ministry of the church. It's meant to be the lifestyle of every believer. The principles of this course should be lived out in the hallways, family rooms and minivans of everyday life.

3. As you experience God changing your heart, you will bring integrity and enthusiasm to personal ministry that cannot be gained any other way. Ask God to reveal things to you. Ask him to change you as you seek to be his instrument of change.

4. Although this course "systematizes" personal ministry, biblical counseling is much more than a system of change. In reality, the most radical difference between biblical counseling and everything else is the belief that people need more than a system of redemption, they need a redeemer! Our real goal is to encourage you to get to know the Lord so that you:

- Rest in his sovereignty.
- Rely on the resources of his grace.
- Practically do his will.

This curriculum is intensely Christ-centered, believing that in him are hidden "all the treasures of wisdom and knowledge" (Colossians 2:3). Look for this emphasis in every lesson.

Let me say again that we are excited that you are embarking on this journey. Remember, we are here to help and support you in any way we can. Our hope is that this course will be just the beginning of a long ministry partnership between CCEF and your church or ministry.

In Christ,

Paul David Tripp
Timothy S. Lane

Course Outline
Helping Others Change

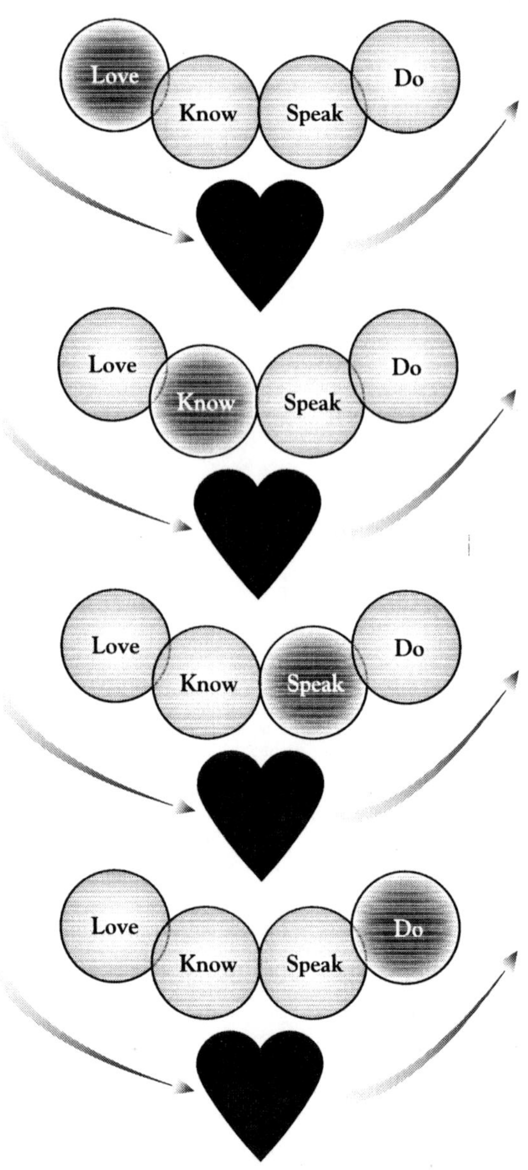

Do We Really Need Help?

DISCUSS HOMEWORK

INTRODUCTION

Let's first become familiar with your workbooks. As you open them you'll see that there are only a few sections. We'll briefly look at each section so that you can easily find your way.

The first thing you'll notice is that there is a page on the inside back cover that summarizes the ***Helping Others Change*** course. The page is entitled ***Helping Others Change: At A Glance.*** We'll be referring to this page often, which is why it is in a place that is easily located. This page gives you a quick preview of the model of growth and ministry that we will be learning: ***LOVE-KNOW-SPEAK-DO.*** The numbers in the diagram indicate the lesson that covers the topic. The ***Course Outline*** also lists each lesson that we'll cover in this course. Next, turn to the ***Word of Welcome*** page at the beginning of the workbook. Take some time later to read this on your own.

We will spend most of our time in the section entitled ***Lesson Content*** (p. 3). You will be using these pages to take notes. The intention of those who developed this course is to minimize the amount of notes you need to take. For those who need and are happiest taking more extensive notes, space has been provided.

The last section, ***Make It Real,*** includes your assignments. Yes, that's right, there will be homework – but relax, it won't be collected or graded. This section will help you interact with the content of each lesson so that you can begin to make it a part of your daily life. This may be the most important section of your workbook because it is the place where you will make the course material your own. You are strongly encouraged to do the assignments so that:

1. You will begin to understand the Christian life better (who I am and who I am before God).
2. You will begin to think biblically about the issues of living.
3. You will improve your ministry skills.

Now let's begin our first lesson by taking a look at ourselves. There are two sides of each of us. All of us are both people in need of help and people who have been positioned by God to provide his help to others. We always carry both identities. The one who needs help is struggling with the issues of living and asking important questions. The helper needs to have a firm understanding of the process of biblical change. That is where we will begin in this lesson.

Look at the next page and you will see a section entitled ***Concepts and Objectives.*** This section is meant to function like a map for each lesson. It will give you a sense of where we're going. Perhaps you've noticed that this section is divided into three parts. ***Concepts*** lists the truths from this lesson that I need to know and remember.

Personalized summarizes how those truths need to be applied to my own life. And ***Related to Others*** points to how each truth sets the agenda for my relationships and for ministry. The initials of these three parts, **CPR,** give us a way of remembering that we are focusing on heart change. By "*Changing Hearts*," God is "*Changing Lives*" – your own and those you serve.

CONCEPTS AND OBJECTIVES

Concept: Our need for help is not the result of the Fall, but the result of being human.

Personalized: I need truth from outside myself to make sense out of life.

Related to others: I need to learn how to be one of God's instruments of change in the lives of others.

LESSON CONTENT

We all come across situations in our own life or in ministry where we don't know what to do or say. It is in these moments that we are confronted with the reality that God hasn't given us a neat system of change that our own wisdom can figure out. Our hope for ourselves and for others can only be found in the presence and work of Jesus the Redeemer. Both the helper and the person in need depend on his wisdom and his power for change.

A Firm Foundation

As we think about our own growth and about serving as God's instruments of change, we need to build a firm biblical foundation for understanding people, their need for help, and how change takes place.

If you were asked to write down a distinctly biblical definition of discipleship or personal ministry, what would you write?

Our culture tends to view personal change as something that requires the help of a professional. But the Bible has a much fuller and more hopeful perspective. The Bible teaches that personal transformation takes place as our hearts are changed and our minds are renewed by the Holy Spirit. And the two instruments that the Holy Spirit uses are the Word of God and the people of God.

Turn to **Isaiah 55:10-13**. This is a beautiful word picture of God's plan to bless us and glorify himself through the changes his Word accomplishes in us. In fact, those changes are a sign of his covenant relationship with us (v.13).

Turn next to **Ephesians 4:11-16**. Here we see that God has given us each other to help us grow to spiritual maturity. Think of all the intricate interdependencies implied by the image of the church as Christ's body. Both of these passages make it clear that God intends to do a powerful work in us. This means that personal change and growth—including radical change of the deepest kind—can take place

- when we allow the Holy Spirit to apply God's Word to our hearts;
- when we allow God's people to encourage, guide, support, pray for, and challenge us in biblical ways.

Few of us have fully tapped the potential for growth and ministry that God has given us with these two resources, but this has been God's plan for us from the beginning. We need a fresh understanding of what the Bible says about this world of personal transformation. We will begin by looking at personal growth and ministry from the vantage point of creation, the Fall, and redemption.

Our Need as Seen in Creation

Follow along with me as I read **Genesis 1:26-28.** Here we see human need in the broadest sense of the term. God knew that even though Adam and Eve were perfect people living in a perfect world in a perfect relationship with God, they could not figure life out on their own. They could not live independent of God's counsel.

God had to explain who they were and what they were to do with their lives and their surroundings. Adam and Eve's need for help was not the result of sin's entrance into the world. They needed God's help because they were human. To be human is to need help outside of oneself in order to understand and live life.

Adam and Eve had this need because there were three things that separated them from the rest of creation:

- They were created by God to be revelation receivers.
- They were created by God to be interpreters.
- They were created by God to be worshippers.

We all are actively interpreting life, and we all share our interpretations with each other. None of us live life based on the facts, but based on our interpretation of the facts. So, to be human is to need truth outside myself in order to make sense out of life. The first instance of help was not person-to-person, but the Wonderful Counselor explaining life to the people he made in his own image.

As we interpret life, we are always expressing some sense of identity. We speak to one another out of some sense of purpose and meaning. We are constantly interpreting life out of a sense of who we are and what we are supposed to be doing, and we are always sharing our interpretations with one another. We all interpret. We are all people of influence.

Our Need as Seen in the Fall

Now turn with me to **Genesis 3:1-7.** Something very dramatic takes place in this passage. For the very first time in human history, we see the entrance of another voice. This new speaker takes the very same set of facts (discussed by God in Genesis 1 and 2) and gives them a very different interpretation.

If Adam and Eve decide to believe the interpretation of this new speaker, it would be stupid to continue to obey God. Notice that our interpretations, our advice giving, are always agenda setting. If you reject the words of God and follow the words of the serpent, you will not think about God, yourself or life in the same way, and you will not continue to do the same things.

What are the principles we can draw out of this passage to develop a biblical understanding of personal growth and ministry?

1. Thoughts, talk, opinions, advice and relationships are always agenda setting. Even though we may be unaware of it, we daily tell one another what to desire, think, and do.

2. Advice is always moral. It always is defining right and wrong, good and bad, true and false, or healthy and unhealthy. Advice always gives our situations and relationships a moral framework.

3. We should hunger for the simple days of Genesis 1 when everything people thought, said, and did was based solely on the words of God. We, however, live in a world of much confusion, where literally thousands of voices speak to us at the same time, each interpreting life and each competing for our hearts.

4. We need Scripture to cut through the confusion and make sense out of life for us.

Our Need as Seen in Redemption

Many people have asked the question, "Do believers, who are indwelt by the Holy Spirit and have the Word of God, really need personal ministry? Isn't the cry for this a lack of faith in the Spirit and a lack of confidence in the Bible?" The final passage we will look at speaks in a powerful way to this question.

Let's look at **Hebrews 3:12-13.** This passage is essentially a warning against falling away from the Lord. The falling away is presented as something that is progressive. Notice the steps:

Sinful (subtle patterns of sin I allow in my life)

Unbelieving (subtle excusing of my sin, backing away from the clear words of Scripture)

Turning away (a loss of my spiritual moorings)

Hardened (heart crusted over with the scabs of sin—no longer tender)

Now what you should ask is, "How could this ever happen to a believer?" This passage declares something about us that explains why this scary warning is necessary. It says that sin is deceitful. And guess who it deceives first!? Us! We have no problem seeing the sin in others.

This is the theology of the passage: As long as sin still dwells within us, there will be some aspect of spiritual blindness in all of us. Yes, we can see the speck of dust in another's eye while missing

the log that is jutting out of our own **(Matthew 7:1-5)**! The passage is basically saying that all of us need help, because until we are at home with the Lord, all of us will suffer from some degree of spiritual blindness. And, unlike physically blind people, spiritually blind people are often blind to their blindness.

So, what the writer of Hebrews says is that we need daily intervention. All of us are in the same place. There are no "haves" and "have nots." Each of us is in need of help and each is called to help, that is, to function daily as one of God's instruments of change in the lives of others.

If this kind of mutual help is going to become a lifestyle, there are two qualities that each of us needs to have. First, we need the courage of honesty. We cannot be afraid of being lovingly honest. We have to love one another enough to break through the walls of spiritual blindness. Second, we need the humility of approachability. We need to be willing to listen and consider when people challenge us with things that alone we would not see. We need to humbly and joyfully embrace the help that God has provided for us.

Three Questions that Everyone Asks

If you live with and care for people, there are three questions that you have probably asked. These three questions form the basis of any system of growth and transformation. They are questions that we must answer in a distinctly biblical way.

1. Why do people do the things they do? To answer this question we need a biblical theology of human motivation. What does the Bible say causes people to think the things they think, to want what they want, or to do the things they do?

2. How does lasting change take place in a person's life? If you see a person doing something that is wrong or destructive, you want to see change take place in his or her life. What does the Bible say leads to such change? We need a biblical theology of change.

The ***How People Change*** curriculum addresses these two questions in depth, beginning in Lessons 2 and 3.

3. How can I be an instrument of change in the life of another person? To answer this question we need a biblical methodology of change.

These are the questions we will be addressing throughout this course. Our goal is that we will all be changed by God, ready to be his instruments of change wherever and with whomever he places us.

THE BIG QUESTION: Why do you need help?

CPR

Concepts

1. To be human is to need help outside of myself.
2. Influence always carries a moral agenda.
3. Everyone suffers from some degree of spiritual blindness.

Personalized

1. I need to receive truth outside of myself to make sense out of life.
2. I need to humbly examine why I do and say the things I do.
3. I need to recognize sin's deceitfulness and commit myself to being approachable.

Related to others

1. I need to learn how to be one of God's instruments of change in the lives of others.
2. I need to saturate myself with Scripture so that my interpretations and counsel to others are based on God's Word.
3. I need to recognize how I am influencing others in the relationships and situations of daily life.

Helping Others Change
Make It Real

LESSON 1

1. How will the truths of this lesson shape your prayers about ministry opportunities?

2. Tell about a time in your life when you responded not to the facts of a situation, but to your interpretation of the facts. Did you realize it at the time?

3. Describe a time when the Lord used a person or the Word of God to reveal your spiritual blindness. What did you learn about your need for such help? If you were helped by a person, what did he or she do to make it a positive or negative experience?

4. What things keep you from being approachable (being helped)? What things keep you from reaching out (helping)? Ask the Lord to help you in these areas and repent where appropriate.

The Heart Is The Target

DISCUSS HOMEWORK

REVIEW

CONCEPTS AND OBJECTIVES

Concept: The heart is active. It shapes and controls our behavior.

Personalized: I must identify what effectively and functionally rules my heart.

Related to others: I must be committed to be an instrument of heart change in the lives of those around me.

LESSON CONTENT

Let's begin by looking at one of the most important word pictures in the New Testament. This word picture is so important because it reveals Christ's perspective on how people function—that is,

why they do the things they do. Turn in your Bibles to **Luke 6:43-46.**

Christ likens the way we function to a tree. If you plant apple seeds and they take root, you don't expect to see peaches or oranges growing. When you are dealing with a plant, you recognize that there is an organic connection between the roots of the plant and the fruit it produces. The same is true with people.

Let's unpack Christ's illustration. In his example, fruit equals behavior. The fruit (behavior) in this passage is speaking. Christ says something very powerful about our words. Our words are literally the heart overflowing. People don't make us say what we say. Situations don't make us say what we say. Our words are shaped and controlled by our hearts. Fruit is what the tree produces, just as our behavior is what our hearts produce. You and I recognize a tree by the kind of fruit it produces.

The second part of the word picture is equally important, but not as obvious. In Christ's example, the roots of the tree equal the heart. This is what is underground. It is not as clearly seen or easily understood. The power of Christ's illustration is in the connection it makes between root and fruit. Christ is saying that the tree has the kind of fruit it does because of the kind of roots it has. The application to us is this: we speak and act the way we do because of what is in our hearts. There may be no more important thing we can say about people and how they function.

You may be asking, "What does all of this have to do with personal growth and ministry?" Christ's word picture sets the direction for both. Let me expand and apply the word picture for you. Pretend that I have an apple tree in my backyard. Each year it buds and grows apples, but when the apples mature, they are dry, wrinkled, brown and pulpy. After several years I decide that it is silly to have an apple tree and never be able to eat its fruit. So I decide that I must do something to "fix" the tree. One Saturday afternoon you look out your window to see me carrying branch cutters, a staple gun, a stepladder, and two bushels of Red Delicious apples into my backyard. You watch as I carefully cut off all the bad apples and

staple beautiful red apples onto the branches of the tree. You come out and ask me what I am doing and I say proudly, "I've finally fixed my apple tree!" What are you thinking about me at this point!?

It is clear that if the tree produces bad apples year after year, there is something wrong with the system of this tree, right down to its very roots. I won't solve the problem by stapling apples onto the tree. What will happen to those new apples? They will rot also because they are not attached to the life-giving roots of the tree.

What does this have to do with personal growth and ministry? The problem with much of what we do to produce growth and change in ourselves and others is that it is nothing more than "fruit stapling." It is a "sin is bad so don't do it" view of change that does not examine the heart behind the behavior. Change that does not reach the heart rarely lasts, but is temporary and cosmetic.

Let's explore the way this passage sets the direction for personal growth and ministry by considering the principles that flow out of it.

1. There is a root and fruit relationship between our heart and our behavior. That is, the heart controls everything I do and say.

2. Lasting change always takes place through the pathway of the heart.

3. Therefore, in personal growth and ministry, heart change is always our goal.

The Question of What Rules the Heart

Maybe you are thinking, "I understand what the Bible says about the heart controlling our behavior, but I don't know what I'm looking for as I examine the heart." Our next passage will help us here. Turn to **Ezekiel 14:1-5.**

Now, let me set the scene for you. The spiritual leaders of Israel have come to the prophet because they have questions that they want to ask God. But as they approach God, he recognizes that something is wrong with them. Look at the passage again. What is wrong with these men?

What is wrong with these men is idolatry. Notice what kind of idolatry. The passage says that they have idols in their hearts. This is deeper and more fundamental than cultural or religious idolatry. An idol of the heart is anything that rules me other than God.

Now, notice God's response. He says that because these men have idols in their hearts, he is going to answer them "in keeping with their great idolatry." God is saying, "Because you have idols in your hearts, the only thing I want to talk about is your idolatry." Why? Maybe they had important questions to ask God. Why would he refuse to talk about anything but the idols?

There is a phrase here that explains God's reaction to these men and explains much to us about how the heart functions. The passage says, "These men have set up idols in their hearts and put wicked stumbling blocks before their faces." (See verse 3.)

Let me illustrate the principle for you. Put your hand up to your face so that you are looking through your fingers. What is happening to your vision? It is obstructed. The only way for your vision to be clear is for your hand to be removed. Here is the unbreakable connection: idol in the heart → stumbling block before the face.

Now let me give you the core principle of this passage. It is the principle of inescapable influence. Whatever rules the heart will exercise inescapable influence over a person's life and behavior.

How does this relate to personal growth and ministry? Let's say you are trying to help a very controlling man who has damaged many relationships in his quest for power. You will not solve his problem by giving him good biblical instruction in communication and conflict resolution. Why? Because as long as the desire for control rules his heart, he will use whatever principles and skills he learns to establish even greater control over the people around him.

If we do not deal with what rules our hearts, we will use even the principles of the Word of God to serve our idols!

Let's examine how the principles of this passage apply to personal growth and ministry.

- Our hearts are always being ruled by someone or something.

- The most important question to ask when examining the heart is, "What is effectively and functionally ruling this person's heart in this situation?"

- Whatever controls my heart will control my reactions and responses to the people and situations in my life.

- The way God changes us is to recapture our hearts to serve him alone.

- The deepest issues of the human struggle are not issues of pain and suffering. The deepest issue is the issue of worship (What really rules my heart?), because what rules our hearts will control the way we respond to both suffering and blessing.

Let's consider two more passages that help us understand this issue. Turn to **Romans 1:25.** Paul makes it very simple for us. He calls idolatry a great exchange. What Paul says here describes us all. We all tend to exchange worship and service of the Creator for worship and service of the creation. What a simple way to explain idolatry! This is what sin is about. The roots of sin in the heart are that we want and love the creation more than the Creator. What really rules our hearts in the situations and relationships of daily living is not love for God, but a craving for some other thing. This exchange (Creator for creation) can take place in any situation or relationship in life. When it does, we will not do what God has called us to do.

The Matter of Treasure

The second passage we want to consider is **Matthew 6:19-24.** Here Christ uses the word treasure to describe what rules our hearts. A treasure is something valuable to us. We all live to gain, maintain, and enjoy our treasures. There are three treasure principles in this passage. The first is assumed and the others are delineated quite clearly.

- Everyone lives for some kind of treasure.
- Whatever you treasure will control your heart. ("Where your treasure is, there your heart will be also.")
- Whatever controls your heart will control your behavior. ("No one can serve two masters.")

The Bible and the Heart

One final consideration is necessary. Maybe you are thinking, "I know that heart change is the goal, but it seems impossible to know the heart. I can only see a person's behavior; I can't look into the heart." Does it seem as if we are discussing the impossible? Then turn in your Bibles to **Hebrews 4:12, 13.**

This passage is about the Bible, and how God uses his Word in our lives. The writer of Hebrews says that the Bible is like God's great scalpel. It is able to cut through all the layers of who I am and what I'm doing to expose my heart. **Hebrews** says that the Bible reveals and judges my heart's thoughts and motives. These are the two most fundamental things our hearts do: Our hearts think and our hearts purpose. They interpret and they desire.

What you and I do is always shaped by these thoughts and motives. They control what we do with the relationships and situations we encounter in daily life.

Here's the encouragement of this passage: Although you cannot see a person's heart, Scripture will expose it to you. The Bible by its very nature is heart-revealing. For that reason, Scripture must be our central tool in personal growth and ministry. It alone can expose and analyze where change needs to take place in our hearts. Remember, heart change *must* take place if we really want changes in our behavior to last.

THE BIG QUESTION: What is your biggest problem?

CPR

Concepts

1. The heart is active. It controls our behavior.

2. Whatever rules the heart exercises inescapable influence over life and behavior. Your heart is always ruled by something.

3. God's Word alone is able to expose and judge the heart.

Personalized

1. If I am committed to personal change and growth, I must be committed to a biblical examination of my heart.

2. In the situations and relationships of my everyday life I must constantly ask, "What is really ruling my heart?"

3. I must always study the Word of God with an eye toward my heart, always asking what the passage reveals about my thoughts and motives. (What is really ruling me?)

Related to others

1. As I minister to others, I want to be an instrument of heart change.

2. Heart change is always the result of the careful ministry of God's Word to a particular person in a specific situation.

3. I must not attempt to manipulate or control the behavior of others. I must leave room for God to work lasting change in their hearts.

Helping Others Change
Make It Real

LESSON 2

1. How will the truths of this lesson shape your prayers about ministry opportunities?

2. Give some examples (good and bad) of your heart overflowing in your words and deeds. What kind of fruit stapling have you tried? When have you seen real change?

3. What are some idols and treasures that challenge the Lord for control of your heart? How have they shaped your interpretations of certain events and relationships in your life?

4. How can God use the things he has taught you in this lesson to enable you to help someone else?

5. Write your best definition of what it means to function as one of God's instruments of change in the life of another.

Understanding Your Heart Struggle

DISCUSS HOMEWORK

REVIEW

CONCEPTS AND OBJECTIVES

Concept: The cause of my struggle is not the people or the situations in my life, but the "heart" that I bring to those relationships and circumstances.

Personalized: I must live with a willingness to examine the true ruling desires of my heart and to learn how those desires shape my responses to people and circumstances.

Related to others: My effectiveness as one of God's instruments of change involves helping others to recognize and confess what really rules them.

LESSON CONTENT

This lesson focuses on two Scripture passages that are windows on the heart struggle of every human being. These passages show us how we end up worshipping and serving the creation rather than the Creator. They demonstrate that what rules the heart powerfully controls how we see and respond to what is around us.

Fights and Quarrels

Turn in your Bibles to **James 4:1-10.** This passage is a detailed illustration of the principles we considered in Lesson 2. James starts with fruit and works down to roots in the heart.

The fruit that James wants us to examine is present in all of our lives. It is human conflict. All of us have a shocking amount of conflict in our lives. It may be fighting over who sits where in the car, or who gets into the bathroom first, or who eats the last chocolate chip cookie. It may be a discouraging disagreement between a husband and wife, or a boss and a worker. James wants us to examine this fruit of conflict by asking, "What causes it?"

Notice that James calls us to do something very different from what we normally do when we are angry. We typically look outside ourselves to explain our anger. ("He makes me so angry!" "If you were the mother of these kids, you'd understand!" "This traffic drives me nuts!") James tells us that if we want to understand our anger, we must examine our hearts.

James says that the "fights and quarrels" we have so constantly are rooted in the desires of our hearts. He says, "Don't they come from the desires that battle within you?" In short, James says, "You fight because of what you want." What a radical perspective this is! People and situations do not make us angry. They only provide the occasion for our anger to express itself.

It is important to understand what James says about the desires of our hearts.

- He does not say it is wrong to desire. When you quit desiring, you are dead! The capacity to desire is God-given and not wrong in itself.

- James does not say that these fights and quarrels are only caused by evil desires.

According to James, how do the desires of our hearts explain the conflicts in our lives? The key phrase is found after the word "desires." James says that our fights and quarrels come from desires that are waging war within our hearts. What is the sole purpose of war? It is control. You see, it is not the fact that we desire that is the problem, but the fact that certain desires wage war in our hearts until they effectively and functionally rule us.

Consider this for a moment. If my heart is ruled by a certain desire, there are only two ways I can respond to you. If you are helping me get what I want, I will be very happy with you and our relationship. But, if you stand in the way of what I want, I will experience anger, frustration and discouragement when I am with you. My problem is not you or the situation we are in together. My problem is that a legitimate desire has taken over my heart and now is in control. It has so much power that it is no longer legitimate. So my response to you is not shaped by God and what he says is best, but by a certain desire that now controls my heart.

Scripture uses the term idolatry to describe a desire that rules my heart. My own idolatry is what causes me to be angry. You stand in the way of what I crave, so I lash out against you in anger. This battle over who or what will rule the heart goes on in all of us all the time. What controls the heart will control the behavior. There is no situation or relationship where this battle is not taking place, because we all tend to "exchange worship and service of the Creator for worship and service of the created thing."

How Desires Take Control

Maybe you're thinking, "How do the normal desires of daily living take control of the heart?" Let's consider the steps:

1. Desire: "I want." Nothing wrong here yet.

2. Demand: "I must." The desire is no longer an expression of love for God and man, but something I crave for myself.

3. Need: "I will." Something desirable is now seen as essential. I am convinced that I cannot live without it.

4. Expectation: "You should." This is where my relationships begin to be affected. If I really believe that this is a need, then it seems right to expect that you will meet my need if you really love me.

5. Disappointment: "You didn't!" Here the anger breaks out and becomes personal. You are standing in the way of what rules my heart.

6. Punishment: "Because you didn't, I will...." I respond to you in anger (silent treatment, hurtful words, vengeance, or violence).

It is important to understand the core principle of this passage, which is found in verse 4. When James says, "You adulterous people," he is not changing the subject. He is explaining why we all struggle with anger. Here is the central principle of this passage: Human conflict is rooted in spiritual adultery. My problem is not sinful people or difficult situations. My problem is that I give the love that belongs to God to someone or something else. My problem is idolatry.

Now, notice the turning point of the passage. Change does not start with trying to control my anger, or being careful with my communication, or remembering conflict resolution principles. James says that change begins as we "submit to God." Only as we confess and forsake our idolatry (desires that have come to rule us) will we live in peace with one another. We are called to "come near to God" and we are promised that he will in turn come near to us.

James says that change involves two things:

- "Wash your hands." This has to do with changes in our behavior.

- "Purify your hearts." This has to do with ridding our hearts of idols.

It is almost impossible to overstate the importance of what this passage teaches. James is essentially saying that you cannot keep the Second Great Command ("Love your neighbor as yourself") if you have not submitted to the First Great Command ("Love the Lord your God …").

A Real Life Illustration

Powerful Emotions and Powerful Desires

There is another passage that explains how our hearts struggle and how that struggle shapes our response to people and situations. Turn to **Galatians 5:13-26.**

This passage falls into four sections: call, struggle, warning, and provision.

The call (v.13) is that we would "serve one another in love." Yet we all recognize how hard this is to do. From the argument over the last cookie to the couple who are convinced they can no longer live together, we find it hard to lovingly serve one another. It is easier for us to demand. It is easier for us to wait to be served. It seems more natural to fight for our place and our rights.

Why is serving others such a struggle? Why does it seem so hard? Why does it demand such sacrifice? Why do so few of us really go through life with an attitude of service?

To understand our difficulty with the call, we have to understand the struggle that lies behind it.

The struggle takes place in our hearts. It is our struggle with our own sinful nature. We struggle because God has not yet completed his work in us. Our struggle is with indwelling sin. In times when we are called to serve another, we indulge our sinful nature instead.

To indulge something means to give in to it or feed it. When you indulge your appetite, you eat. So, instead of giving in to God's call, we give in to the desires and demands of the sinful nature.

Verse 24 explains what Paul means when he talks about indulging the sinful nature. It means that you give in to its passions and desires. This means that in certain relationships and situations, my responses are not being controlled by the Lord and his will. Instead, I am being ruled by powerful emotions (passions) and powerful cravings (desires). So fear, anger, discouragement, the desire to belong, the desire to be affirmed, etc. set the agenda for my behavior rather than the Lord.

This leads us to the warning in the passage. Paul warns us that we can destroy each other. We can smash another's hope. We can crush another's faith. We can break another's spirit. The fact is that our actions do make a difference. Our responses to each other are either productive or destructive. It is unbiblical to say that the unkind word, the thoughtless action, the selfish initiative make no difference. We are always influencing each other, one way or the other.

God's Provisions for the Struggle

How will we ever defeat the sinful nature? How will we find the strength to fight its control? How can we say "no" to the powerful emotions and desires that rise up within us? The answer to these questions is not found in our strength, but in God's provision.

Paul directs us to two things God gives us so that we can say "no" to the passions and desires of the sinful nature and serve one another in love.

1. We have been crucified with Christ. (See verse 24.) Paul is calling us to remember our union with Christ. This union means that when Christ died, I died. When Christ rose, I, too, rose to a new life where sin's power over me has been forever broken. Now I have the power to resist its control.

   This means that we do not have to be ruled by powerful emotions and desires. We can resist them and respond to one another in servant love.

2. We have been given the Warrior Spirit. (See **Galatians 5:16-18.**) Why this name? Because the Holy Spirit, who dwells in us, fights on our behalf. Paul is literally saying here that the Spirit is an adversary who stands opposed to the sinful nature. God knew that our natures are so weak, and the conflict within so powerful, that he could not leave us to ourselves. He sent his Spirit to literally live inside us so that, by his power, we would be able to defeat the passions and desires of our sinful nature.

   Because the power of sin has been broken and the Holy Spirit has been given, we can say "no" to powerful emotions and powerful desires and be free to serve each other in love.

THE BIG QUESTION: As you deal with your daily situations and relationships, what things tend to control your heart?

CPR

Concepts

1. What a person does and says is not caused by the people and situations around him.

2. A person's behavior is always controlled by the desires that rule his heart.

3. We have been united with Christ and indwelt by the Holy Spirit so that we can say "no" to the passions and desires of the sinful nature.

Personalized

1. When attempting to understand my emotions, words and actions, I must always examine my own heart.

2. I must learn to ask myself what emotions and desires control me in the various relationships and situations of daily life.

3. I must learn to affirm my identity in Christ and rely on the indwelling Holy Spirit as I seek to serve others in love.

Related to others

1. I must not blame people or circumstances for my emotions, words, and actions.

2. I must always remember that the desires that rule my heart will shape the way I relate to the people in my life. I must constantly ask myself if those relationships are characterized by demanding or serving.

3. I must be committed to helping people remember who they are in Christ as they struggle with temptations to indulge the sinful nature.

Helping Others Change
Make It Real

LESSON 3

1. Study the following passages to see how Jesus looked beyond external behavior to the heart.

Passage	Situation	What Jesus discerned about the heart
Matt. 8:23-27	Disciples in boat with Jesus.	
Matt. 12:38-39	Pharisees request a sign.	
Matt. 16:21-23	Peter rejects the idea that Jesus will suffer.	
Matt. 22:15-22	Pharisees try to trap Jesus.	
Mark 7:1-23	Pharisees and "unclean" hands.	
Mark 10:17-23	Rich young man.	
Luke 9:46-48	Dispute over who is greatest.	
Luke 10:38-42	Mary and Martha.	
Luke 15:1-2, 11-32	Parable of the Lost Son.	
John 4:1-26	Woman at the well.	
John 6:1-14,25-58	Feeding of the five thousand.	
John 8:1-11	Woman caught in adultery.	

Passage	Situation	What Jesus discerned about the heart
John 13:1-17	Jesus washes disciples' feet.	
John 21:15-19	Jesus reinstates Peter.	

2. Examine your heart in the light of these passages.
   If Christ were talking to you, what would he seek to expose?
   Where is he calling you to fundamental heart change?
   Pray about these things.

Following the Wonderful Counselor

DISCUSS HOMEWORK

REVIEW

CONCEPTS AND OBJECTIVES

Concept: Effective personal ministry seeks to be part of what the Lord is doing in the lives of others by modeling the way he has worked in us.

Personalized: I must examine the way I seek to stimulate change in those around me. Are the things I do consistent with the example of the Wonderful Counselor?

Related to others: I must think redemptively about my relationships. That is, I always look for the opportunities he is giving me to be part of his work of change.

LESSON CONTENT

Have you ever known that a friend needed to change, but you simply did not know how to help? Have you ever tried to help and felt like you made things worse? Have you ever felt like you wanted to help someone, but you were in over your head?

When our culture thinks about helping a person change, it usually thinks in formal and professional terms. If you accept that model, you will probably conclude two things:

1. That the Bible doesn't say much about how to help a person change.

2. That the average Christian has no business trying to help someone change.

Many Christians have bought into the cultural model and, as a result, become passive and uninvolved in the needs that surround them. It's not that they don't care. It's that they don't know what to do, and if they did, they don't think they should do it.

Called to be Ambassadors

Scripture gives us a very different model. First, it calls each of us to function as Christ's ambassadors (**2 Corinthians 5:14-21**). An ambassador is a representative. This is exactly what we are all called to be in all of our relationships. We are placed in these relationships not only so that our lives would be happy and satisfying, but more importantly so that we would represent the Lord as he is working change in others' lives.

The work of an ambassador includes three important points of focus. As an ambassador I will represent:

- The message of the King. An ambassador is always asking, "What does my Lord want to communicate to this person in this situation?"

- The methods of the King. This is the "how" of the ambassadorial calling. How does the Lord work change in our lives? What are his methods? I want to work as he has worked.

- The character of the King. Here I am focusing on "why" the Lord does what he does. I want to faithfully represent his attitudes.

Happily, the second thing that Scripture does is to liberally display the work of the King for us. As we read the Bible, we hear his message over and over again (**Matthew 5-7; Luke 15-18**). As we read the Bible, we are confronted with his methods again and again (**John 3:1-21; 4:1-26; Luke 9:18-27; 10:25-37**). And the pages of Scripture are filled with the beauty of his character (**Philippians 2:1-12; Ephesians 4:29-5:2; 1 Peter 2:23**). These three things define how we can be useful instruments in the hands of Christ, our model and our king. We accept our calling as ambassadors and faithfully seek to represent his message, methods and character wherever and with whomever he places us.

Turn to Figure 4-1. This illustration is meant to capture what it means to function as one of Christ's ambassadors of change in someone's life.

First, you will notice that on the left side of the page are the words "Negative Fruit." This pictures the problems that get us involved in personal ministry. God opens our eyes to a harvest of bad fruit in a person's life. It may be a broken relationship. It may be anger, fear, or discouragement. It may be an act of gossip or vengeance. God allows us to see someone thinking, behaving, or responding in a wrong way. Or perhaps a struggling person reveals these things to us and asks for our help. However it happens, we are exposed to a harvest of bad fruit in someone's life.

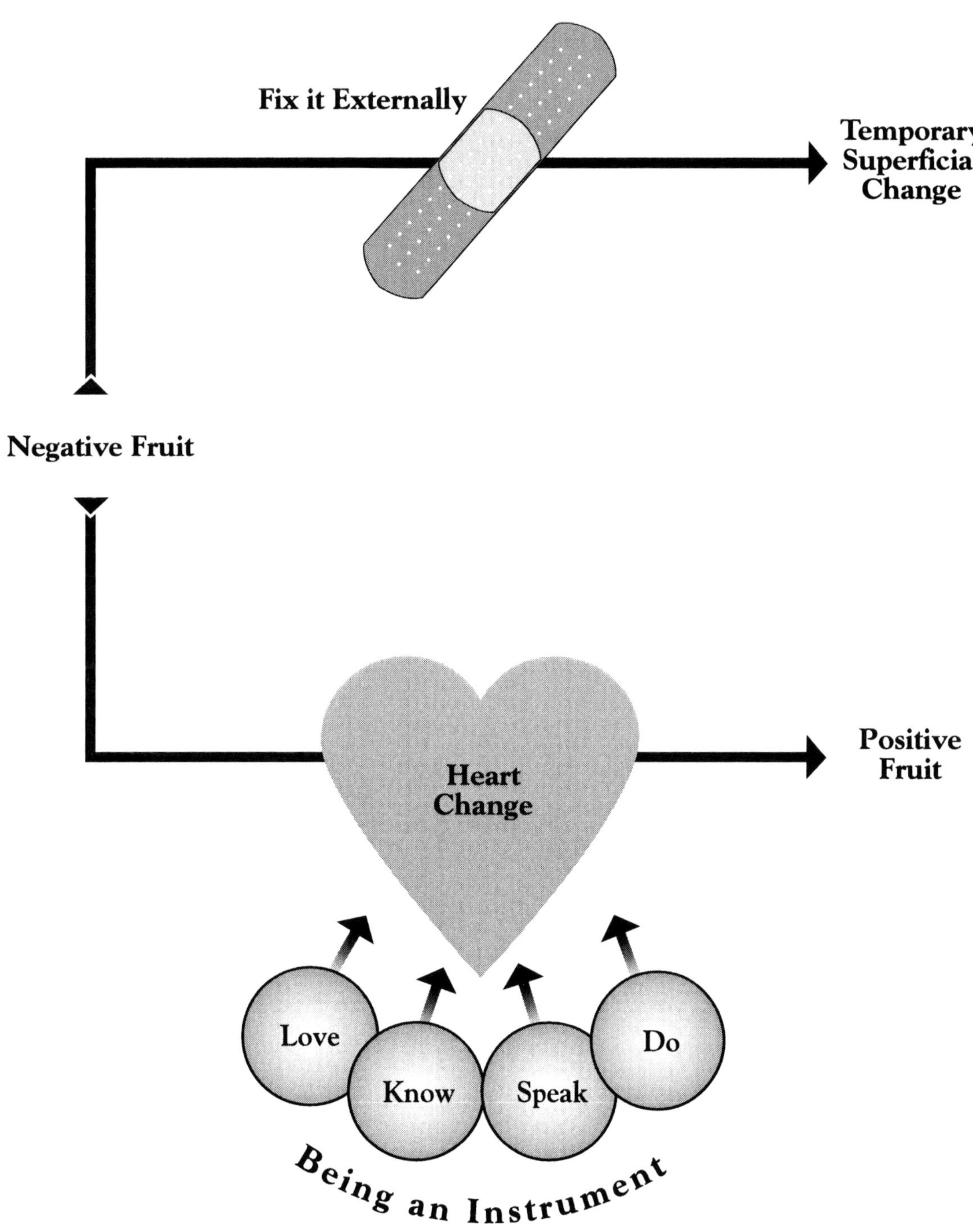

Figure 4-1. Serving as an Instrument of Change.

On the right side of the diagram are the words "Positive Fruit." This is our goal. Our purpose is to be used of God to produce a harvest of good fruit in the person's life, even though he or she may remain in the exact same situation with the exact same people.

The bandage at the top middle of the diagram summarizes the goal most people have when they seek help. Yes, they want things to change, but they seldom have their hearts in view. They basically have an externalistic view of change. They want a change in their circumstances, change in another person, or change in their emotions. They think that if "things" would change, they would be much better. But the result, as the illustration shows, is seldom more than temporary and superficial change. It's true that there are often elements in a situation that need to be changed, but we cannot stop there. Our goal is to lead people to a deeper, fuller view of change. This is why the heart (with the arrows pointing to it) is at the bottom middle of the diagram. We believe that lasting change always takes place through the pathway of the heart. The heart is our target. Heart change is our goal.

We finally come to the four circles with the heading "Being An Instrument." The four words in the circles—***LOVE-KNOW-SPEAK-DO***—describe God's way of change. This is our model for functioning as an instrument of real heart change in a person's life. This model takes seriously our need for heart change and our need to follow the example of Christ.

As you look at the diagram, don't think that you are learning a four-step process. The four circles represent four aspects of a personal ministry relationship, four ways to get involved in someone's life. As God gives you ministry opportunities, you will be doing all four things simultaneously.

Let's examine each element separately.

Love

The ***LOVE*** function points out the importance of relationship to the process of change. You could argue biblically that change always takes place in the context of a relationship. Theologians call this a covenantal model of change. God comes and makes a covenant with us. He commits himself to being our God and he takes us as his people. And in the context of that relationship, he accomplishes his work of radically changing us. As we understand the work of God in our own lives, we realize that our relationship to him is not a luxury. It is a necessity. It provides the only context in which the lifelong process of change can take place in us. In the same way, we are called to build strong and godly relationships with one another. God's purpose for these relationships is that they would be workrooms for him. It is important, therefore, that we learn how to build relationships in which his work of change can thrive.

Know

KNOW has to do with really getting acquainted with the people around us. Many of the people we think we know we really don't know. We know facts about them (who their spouse is, where they work, some likes and dislikes, their children, etc.), but we really don't know the person inside the skin. Our relationships are often trapped in the casual and because of this, our opportunities to minister effectively are limited.

Knowing a person really means knowing the heart. When I say I am getting to know you better, I'm not gaining a more intimate understanding of your nose or arm! I mean that I know more about your beliefs and goals, your hopes and dreams, your values and desires. If I know you, I will be able to predict what you will think and how you will feel in a given situation. A friendship is really the connection of hearts.

Christ was so committed to an accurate knowledge of our hearts that he entered our world and lived here for thirty-three years. He faced everything we face so that we could come to him knowing that he understands our struggle (**Hebrews 4:14-16**).

So, the **KNOW** function gets us below the surface of the casual. It teaches us how to gather the information necessary to know a person at the level of his heart. And as we get to know the person, we help him to know himself more accurately and clearly.

Speak

SPEAK involves bringing God's truth to bear on this person in this situation. To do this we need to ask, "What does God want this person to see that he or she is not seeing? How can I help him see it?"

The Gospels are full of brilliant examples of the way Christ helped people to see the truth. Through stories and questions, he broke through their spiritual blindness and helped them to see the reality of who they were and the glory of what he could do for them.

Speaking the truth in love does not mean making grand pronouncements. Rather, it means helping a person to see his life clearly. For lasting change to take place, a person must see himself accurately in the mirror of God's Word. It is also vital that he accurately sees God, and the resources for change he has provided.

Do

Finally, we must help the person to ***DO*** something with what he has learned – to apply the insights God has given to his or her daily life and relationships. Insight alone is not change. It is the beginning of change. The insights God gives us about who we are, who he is, what he has provided for us, and what he has called us to do must be applied to practical, specific realities of everyday life.

Christ calls us not just to be hearers of his Word, but to be active doers as well. As Christ's ambassadors, we are meant to help others respond in practical, personal ways to this call.

Something further needs to be said about the ***LOVE-KNOW-SPEAK-DO*** model of personal ministry. This is not just an aspect of the ministry of the local church, but a lifestyle to which God has called each one of us. God has called us to be the life-changing instruments of his grace in each situation and in every relationship. This lifestyle will work in the formal counseling office as well as in an informal conversation with a struggling Christian friend. This ministry model can be easily adapted to whatever opportunities God gives you to function as one of his instruments of change.

THE BIG QUESTION: Right now, where has God positioned you to be one of his instruments of change?

CPR

Concepts

1. God calls us to be ambassadors, representing his message, methods, and character (**2 Corinthians 5:14-21**).

2. Ambassadors get from negative fruit to positive fruit not by fixing problems externally, but by heart change.

3. The ***LOVE-KNOW-SPEAK-DO*** model follows Christ's example of how to do this (**John 13:34**).

Personalized

1. In all of my relationships, I must remember that I am Christ's ambassador.

2. I must examine my goals for my relationships. Am I solely motivated by my own personal happiness? Do I respond to others with a desire to encourage God's work of change in their lives?

3. I must examine my commitment to the message, methods, and character of the King.

Related to others

1. I must learn to look at all of my relationships redemptively, keeping an eye out for God-given moments of ministry.

2. It is important to use the ***LOVE-KNOW-SPEAK-DO*** model as a way to examine the quality of the relationships God has given me.

3. In my relationships, I must always remember that I am called to be God's instrument. God alone changes people.

Helping Others Change
Make It Real

LESSON 4

1. What are some reasons why external change is appealing to us as human beings? Why does God seek heart change?

2. How has God dealt with you according to the ***LOVE-KNOW-SPEAK-DO*** model? How have others done ***LOVE-KNOW-SPEAK-DO*** with you? Pick a specific instance.

3. Reflect (using this model) on two or three relationships in your life. Where are they weak? Where are they strong? Have you been functioning as an ambassador? Pray that God would use these truths to shape the way you serve in these relationships.

4. **Personal Ministry Opportunity**

Throughout the rest of ***Helping Others Change***, you will begin a process in which you will apply what you have learned about **LOVE, KNOW, SPEAK, DO**. The ***Make It Real*** section of every lesson will help you to think about a specific personal setting where you can apply what you learn. We hope that you will find this challenging and exciting. Thinking about a particular ministry opportunity can spur you to make changes in your relationships in some everyday situation.

First, choose a setting where you want to concentrate your attention. You could choose a formal or an informal relationship, a 1:1 relationship or a small group.

- You could choose a setting whose stated purpose is Christian nurture: a Sunday school class, a Bible study group, a discipling relationship, or a small group.

- You could choose a person you live with: a family member or roommate.

- You could choose a more casual setting: a friendship; conversation after church or over coffee; conversations at work over lunch; contacts in your neighborhood or at an athletic event.

- You could choose a work group: a board of elders or deacons, the choir, a missions or worship committee, a team of Sunday school teachers, an evangelistic team, co-workers on a task force, or a study group at school.

Whatever you choose, seek to become more biblically intentional in your communication.

Second, describe and analyze the setting and the person or people involved. Who are the members (including you!)? What actually happens when you get together? What are the typical communication patterns? If you are focusing on a small group, what is its history? What are its stated or assumed purposes? What is the leadership structure, formal or informal? What roles do people fill? What agenda or goals—stated or unstated—operate in each person and in the group as a whole? What are the current strengths and weaknesses of the group from a biblical standpoint?

Third, as you work through the rest of the lessons, begin to strategize. Design a plan for ministry on the basis of what you have been studying and thinking. How will you bring about an increasingly biblical ministry? How will you act and speak differently? What does the Bible say about you and the relationship or group? Allow the teaching you will receive in Lessons 5-12 to inform you as you take advantage of this ministry opportunity.

Fourth, pray! As you study each lesson, don't simply think of the truths as strategies for happier relationships. See them as a means to see your own need for change and your dependence upon Christ to live in a way that evidences him. You may want to ask two or three people to pray for you in this process. (This exercise was developed by David Powlison as a class assignment in "Counseling in Everyday Life." It has been adapted for this curriculum).

LOVE I: Building Relationships in which God's Work Will Thrive

DISCUSS HOMEWORK

1. What does the Bible say about how people change?

2. What four elements of the biblical model of personal ministry were presented in Lesson 4? What did you learn about your strengths and weaknesses?

REVIEW

In **Lesson 1** we learned that we all need HELP:

1. Human beings need truth outside themselves to understand life.

2. Influence and advice always carry a moral agenda.

3. Spiritual blindness affects us all. We need to be willing to give help and receive it.

In **Lesson 2** we learned that the ***HEART*** is the target:

1. The idols that rule the heart will shape the life and behavior.

2. The Bible is God's mirror to reveal our hearts, so we must be committed to examining our hearts biblically.

3. You must change the root (the heart) to change the fruit (behavior).

In **Lesson 3** we learned about the ***HOPE*** in our union with Christ:

1. People and situations do not control what we say and do.

2. Our heart's desires control our behavior.

3. When we are united with Christ and indwelt by the Holy Spirit, we can say "No" to the passions and desires of the sinful nature.

In **Lesson 4** we learned that we are ***AMBASSADORS***:

1. Our ministry will be effective when it reflects the way the Wonderful Counselor works in our lives.

2. As God's ambassadors, we are to represent his message, methods, and character.

3. The ***LOVE-KNOW-SPEAK-DO*** model reflects Christ's example and helps us gauge our effectiveness in relationships.

CONCEPTS AND OBJECTIVES

Concept: God always changes people in the context of relationships based on love.

Personalized: I must build relationships in which love provides a context for God's work of change.

Related to others: Biblical love demands a higher agenda for my relationships than making myself and the other person happy.

LESSON CONTENT

What would you say in response to this question: "What role do relationships play in ministry?" Are the relationships God gives us mere luxuries, wonderful gifts from a loving God to bring us happiness? Or does the Bible present a higher agenda? God's plan for our relationships is what this lesson is about.

God's relationship with us is loving and redemptive. Our salvation in Christ opens the door for us to have relationships with others that reflect those qualities. Perhaps you are thinking, "I understand the words, but I am not sure what you mean." To say that God wants our relationships to be loving and redemptive means three things:

- That he has a higher goal for our friendships than our present, personal happiness.
- That he wants our relationships to provide a context for his ongoing work of change in and through us.
- That we need to build relationships that promote and encourage this work of change.

Our Relationship with God

There is no better way to understand the important role of relationships than to consider the way Christ works in our own lives. Look at **Figure 5-1**, which captures the importance of relationship in God's work of personal change.

The pathway represents our life. The two doors, labeled justification and adoption, represent the two things Christ did to bring us into relationship with God and make us his children. These words explain how we enter into relationship with God.

In justification by faith, God declares me to be righteous based on the perfect life, death, and resurrection of Christ. In justification, Christ's righteousness is credited to my account. Justification is important because my sin separates me from God. Justification removes my sin and gives me Christ's righteousness, making me acceptable to God and thus able to have a relationship with him.

Adoption also involves my relationship with God. Not only does God justify me, he adopts me. He welcomes me into his family with all the rights and privileges of being his child. Justification and adoption give me a full and complete relationship with God.

As a result of justification and adoption, am I okay? This is a trick question. If you are talking about my standing or relationship with God, the answer is "yes." Nothing needs to be added to Jesus' work. If you are talking about my condition as a person, the answer is "no." I still struggle with sin, and there is still radical change that needs to take place in me, so that I can be what God has chosen me to be and do what he has chosen me to do (pictured by the baby maturing into an adult). That lifelong process of change is called sanctification. Sanctification is the process by which God actually makes me what he legally declared me to be in justification—holy.

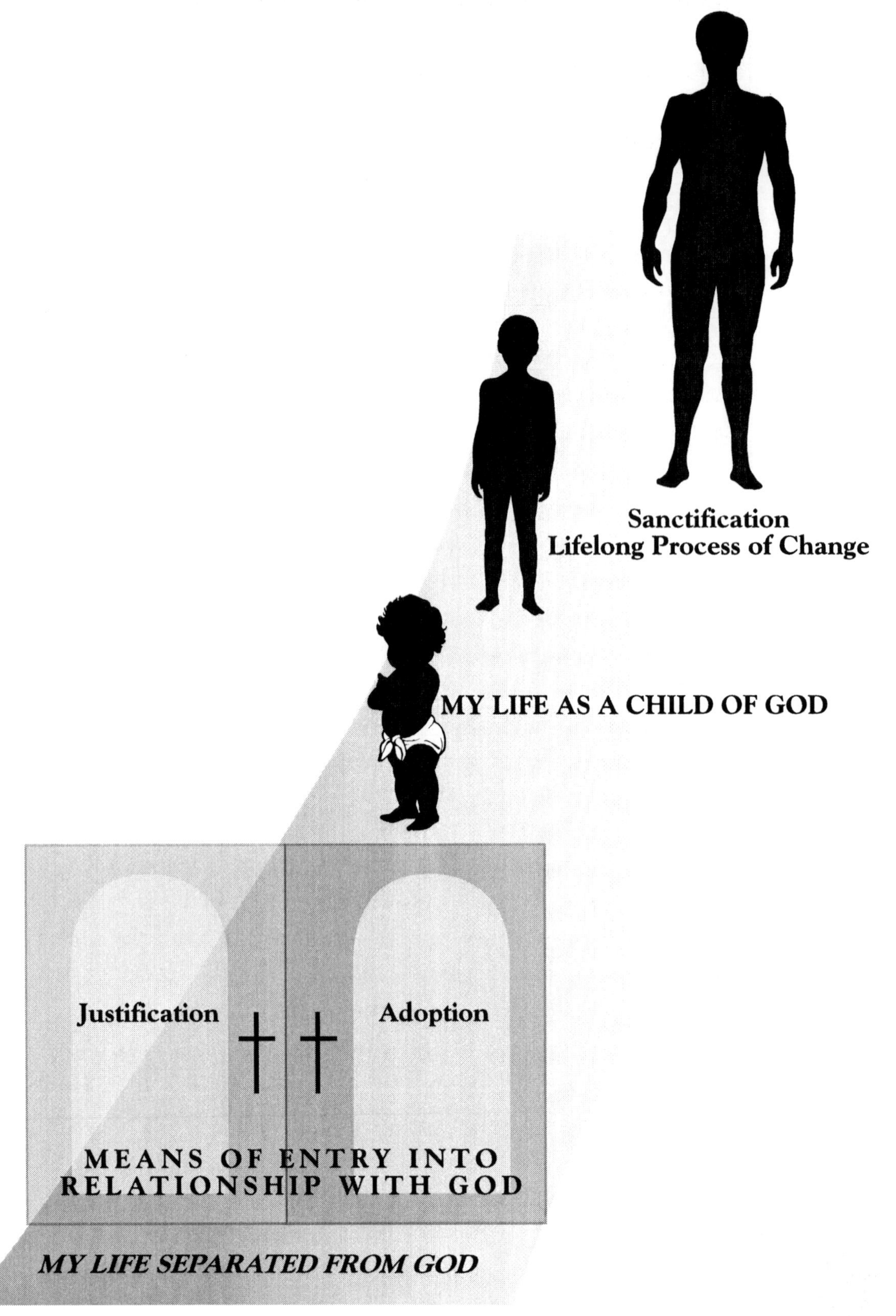

Figure 5-1. The Relational Foundation for Ministry: Salvation as Our Model.

God doesn't justify and adopt me because I am okay, but precisely because I am not okay. He knows that lasting change will take place in me only when I am in a personal relationship with him. In his love, he makes that relationship a reality. Only those who have a relationship with God through justification and adoption will undergo the radical change process of progressive sanctification.

The way Christ loves us and works to change us is our model as we love others and work with them. We too want to begin by building relationships of love, grace, and trust with others. This is a covenantal view of change. In the biblical model, relationships are not a luxury, but a necessity. They are where redemptive activity always takes place.

Let's recap:

- Redemptive activity always takes place in the context of relationships.
- God's first step in changing us is to draw us into relationship with him.
- Our relationships are an essential part of the work of change God is completing in us and in others.

Four Elements of a Loving Relationship

Look at **Figure 5-2.** The oval represents one of your relationships. The four words summarize four ways to demonstrate love to someone and build a relationship that promotes God's work of change.

1. Enter the person's world.
2. Incarnate the love of Christ.
3. Identify with suffering.
4. Accept with agenda.

We will discuss each of these elements of love in detail.

1. Enter the Person's World

How do you build a personal ministry relationship? How can you be used by God to help people to seek his help? Why do we tend to miss so many ministry opportunities?

When we seek to capture God-given opportunities for ministry, we have to recognize the entry gates God gives us. A gate is a means of entry from one thing to another. What are the entry gates from a casual relationship to a life-changing ministry relationship?

Let's talk about what an entry gate is not.

- It is not the problem that the person wants to talk about.
- It is not a situation or circumstance in his life.
- It is not another person or a problem in a relationship.

No, an entry gate is this particular person's experience of the situation, problem, or relationship. To recognize the entry gate you need to ask, "What is this person struggling with in the midst of the situation?" Or, "What has this person in its grip right now?"

Here is an example. A woman has been married for fifteen years and has three children. She awakens one morning to find that her husband is gone. In a note, he announces that he has left the marriage. He has fallen in love with someone else, taken his clothes, emptied the bank account, and hired a lawyer. She calls you on the phone. Ask yourself, what has this woman in its grip? What is she struggling with right now? The obvious answer is fear. She is flooded with terrifying questions, the scariest being, "Why would God let this happen to me?"

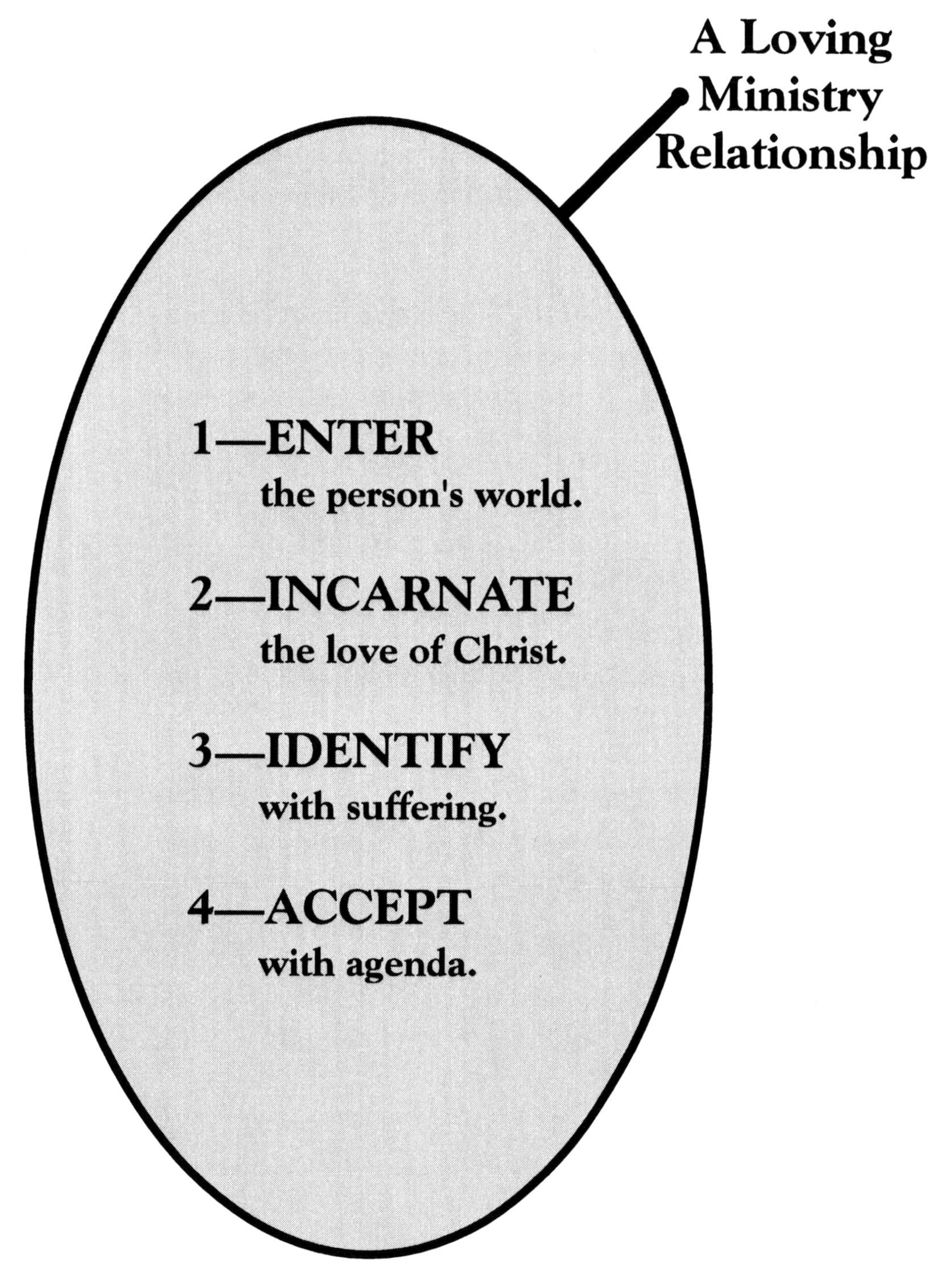

Figure 5-2. The Four Elements of a Loving Ministry Relationship.

In this situation, fear is the entry gate. It gives you a wonderful opportunity to show love and build a ministry relationship with this woman. So often we address a problem and miss the person in the middle of his or her unique struggle. We address situations and miss the war for the heart going on inside. However, when we recognize these entry gate opportunities and speak to them, people respond, "This person has heard me. This person understands me. I want more of this kind of help." This is the power of a loving relationship.

Remember, an entry gate is not the problem or situation itself, but the way in which this person is struggling with the problem. (It might be fear, anger, guilt, anxiety, hopelessness, aloneness, envy, discouragement, desires for vengeance, etc.)

Three things will result from recognizing and responding to the entry gate issues:

- The building of horizontal trust. The person feels understood and is therefore ready to trust you and tell you more.

- The strengthening of vertical hope. As I represent God's sympathetic, understanding love and show how the Bible speaks to the deepest issues of a person's experience, the person will grow in her hope in the Lord's presence, promises, and power.

- The beginning of a commitment to the process of change. The person says, "This has already been helpful. I want more of this kind of help."

How do you get beyond the problem and connect with the person? How do you recognize an entry gate issue? Here are three ways to identify the person's particular struggle in the midst of the situation.

- Listen for emotive words. ("I am so scared." "I am totally discouraged." "This makes me so angry!")
- Listen for interpretive words. ("I guess I deserve this." "This always happens to me." "God just doesn't hear me.")
- Listen for self talk. ("I am such a failure." "I'm tired of being such a doormat!" "I feel like quitting altogether.")

Here are some entry gate questions you might ask this woman as you talk with her and build a relationship. (It would be unlikely that you would ask all these questions at once, especially when she first calls you.)

"What came into your mind when you read the note?"
"What are you struggling with most right now?"
"Are you facing something you thought you would never face? What are you feeling?"
"What are you afraid of right now?"
"Are you feeling angry? Where is that a real struggle?"
"How are you connecting with God right now? Do you have any sense of who he is and what he is doing?"
"Do you feel hopeless? Do you feel like God is asking you to do the impossible as you deal with this?"
"What questions do you wish you could ask your husband?"
"What questions do you wish you could ask God?"
"When you can't sleep, what thoughts keep you awake?"
"What part of this situation is getting to you the most?"
"Do you find yourself struggling with regrets?"

There is no shortage of ministry opportunities around us. Our real problem is that we do not know how to take advantage of them all. But we can learn to recognize these opportunities and use them to build loving relationships that encourage God's work of change.

2. Incarnate the Love of Christ

How does God use us to change people? Is it just through the things we say? Is change simply a matter of confronting people with the truth and calling them to obey? Or does God use us in other ways?

Take a moment now to reflect on the people God has used in your life. In the space provided, write the ways God used them to change your life. No doubt God used their words — their conversation, advice, and confrontation. But what other aspects of the relationship did God use to encourage change in you? Highlight those nonverbal elements as you write.

If we are taking our role as ambassadors seriously, we have to say that God changes people not just through what we say, but through who we are and what we do. During his ministry on earth Jesus said, "If you have trouble believing what I say, then look at the things I have done. They are all the evidence that you need" (paraphrase of passages like **John 14:11**). As ambassadors, we are not only called to speak the truth but to incarnate it — to be real, living, flesh-and-blood illustrations of it. We are not just God's spokespersons; we are his evidence. Our transformed lives testify to the power of his grace to transform hearts. God will transform people not just through what we say, but also through the way we display the love God has shown to us and to them. We want to incarnate his love in the relationships he has given us.

Turn to **Colossians 3:15-17.** Here is one of the New Testament's clearest calls to personal ministry. We are called to have Scripture so deeply a part of us that we are wise and thankful, and therefore constantly prepared to teach and admonish (confront) one another. But you really don't understand this passage if you start with verse 15. You must start with verse 12.

In these verses Paul uses a very important metaphor, the metaphor of clothing. Clothing is important because it covers us. Clothing identifies us. Clothing describes our function. Paul is reminding us that what we wear to moments of personal ministry is as important as what we say. ("Wear" here does not refer to physical clothes, but the clothing of a Christlike character.) Essentially, Paul is saying, "If you are going to be involved in what I am doing in the lives of others, come dressed for the job."

What is that clothing? These are not just isolated items of character. The qualities listed here add up to the character of Christ. Paul is saying, "You are called to put on Christ as you minister to others." God changes people not simply because you have said the hard words of truth to them, but because those strong words were said with compassion, kindness, humility, gentleness, patience, and love. When we do this, we actually become the physical evidence of the very things we are presenting to others. When this happens, we are not only incarnating truth, we are incarnating Christ, who is with us and our only hope.

The incarnational aspect of ministry is important because God uses who we are to convey his truth, as well as what we say. But our relationship with another person is important for another reason as well. In personal ministry, the sin of the person you are ministering to will be revealed in your relationship. If you are ministering to an angry person, at some point that anger will be directed at you. If you are in a relationship with a person who is struggling with trust, at some point she will distrust you. A depressed person will tell you he tried everything you are suggesting and it didn't work. You might think of it this way: you can't stand next to a puddle without eventually being splashed by the mud!

Galatians 6:1 says, "Brothers, if someone is caught in a sin, you who are spiritual should restore him gently. But watch yourself, or you also may be tempted." (See also **1 Timothy 4:16.**) We need to watch our reactions to the people we are serving, since they will often sin against us in the same way they sin against others. How do we respond when we are sinned against? Are we responding in love? As the person's sin and struggle become part of our experience, are we demonstrating the power of Christ's transforming grace in our response? Are we incarnating Christ as we deal with sin in our ministry and relationships?

Sometimes we will live up to our calling as Christ's ambassadors; at other times we will fail. Even then, we can minister effectively if we apply the gospel to our own lives by confessing our sin, asking forgiveness from God (and the other person, if appropriate) and claiming God's strength to serve him faithfully.

Remember, we are called to be ambassadors. An ambassador not only faithfully delivers the message of the King, but incarnates his character as well. Personal ministry to suffering sinners will always mean sacrifice and suffering for us, so we must be aware of our responses to those trials. In the midst of ministry struggle, are we representing the King well? Are we willing to die to ourselves to see life in this other person? We are not only called to be a conduit of God's truth, but an evidence of it as well.

THE BIG QUESTION: Are you building relationships in which God's work of change can thrive?

CPR

Concepts

1. Change takes place in the context of relationships.

2. People's struggles provide entry gates that help us build relationships promoting God's work of change.

3. God uses not only what I say, but how I incarnate the love of Christ to encourage change in others' lives.

Personalized

1. Are my relationships motivated by a desire for personal happiness or a desire for God's work of change?

2. Do I search for (and take advantage of) the entry gate opportunities God gives me?

3. Do I seek not only to be a spokesman for the transforming power of God's grace, but the evidence of it as well?

Related to others

1. Right now, where is God revealing the struggles of others to me? Am I entering these gates of opportunity?

2. What motivates me most in my current relationships — God's work of change or my own idea of self-centered happiness?

3. In my current relationships, where is God giving me opportunities to demonstrate (by my character and my living) God's power to transform hearts?

Helping Others Change
Make It Real

LESSON 5

1. As you think about your ***Personal Ministry Opportunity***, how might you revise your goals? In what ways have your goals been less than redemptive? In what ways have you either failed to accept the person or given up on a godly agenda for change? Make your responses a matter of consistent prayer.

2. What entry gates into the experience of the person or group have you chosen? Write down some questions that would help you enter the person's or group's world with understanding and love.

3. What might it look like for you to incarnate Christ's love to that person? Try to think of ways that don't involve words! What character qualities do you need to exhibit? Think about examples where others have done this for you.

LOVE II: Building Relationships in which God's Work Will Thrive

DISCUSS HOMEWORK

REVIEW

1. What entry gate opportunities did God give you this week? How did you handle them?

2. Where did God call you to incarnate his love? What was the situation? What did you do?

CONCEPTS AND OBJECTIVES

Concept: God calls us to suffer so that we would be qualified agents of his comfort and compassion.

Personalized: I need to ask, "Where has God led me through suffering and what has he taught me through it?"

Related to others: I need to look for the sufferers that God has placed in my path. Have I functioned in their lives as God's agent of comfort?

LESSON CONTENT

In this lesson we begin to look at the remaining two aspects of love in a ministry relationship pictured in **Figure 5-2**. The first is:

3. Identify with Suffering

Have you ever gone through a hard time and felt completely alone? Have you ever, in the middle of suffering, wondered if you were the only one who had gone through such a thing? Have you ever thought, in the middle of difficulty, that the people around you didn't really care? Have you gone through things that made you wonder if God cared?

One of the predictable realities of life in a fallen world is suffering. It is everywhere around us. It has touched each of our lives. Suffering is both a tool of redemption and an occasion for great temptation. Suffering is the common ground of personal ministry. It is the thing we share with everyone we meet.

Turn to **Hebrews 2:10-11.** This passage points to the importance of recognizing the commonality of suffering. Notice once again that Christ is our model here. This passage is about how Christ, "the author of our salvation," identifies with us. It says that Christ is not ashamed to call us "brothers." Pay attention to the nature of this term. The title "brother" not only connotes family relationship, it connotes sibling relationship. A sibling is an equal. To say you are my brother means:

- We are in the same family.
- We are in a similar position in the family.
- We share the same life experiences because of that position.

This should be the character of our personal ministry. It does not have that "I stand above you as one who has arrived" character. The character of personal ministry is humility. It flows out of the humble recognition that we share an identity. I am not a finished product. God has not completed his work in me. We stand as brothers in the middle of God's lifelong process of change. I am not this person's guru. I am not what he or she needs. Change will not happen simply because he is exposed to my wisdom and experience. We share identity, we share experience, and we are of the same family.

But we need to go further here. Look back at the **Hebrews** passage. What is the center, the core of our brotherhood? What is the thing we have in common with Christ? The answer is suffering.

Notice that verse 10 says something very interesting (and a bit confusing) about Christ. It says that, like us, he was made perfect through suffering. The writer is explaining how Christ shares identity with us, and making a connection between Christ's life and ours. The connection is found in the words "should make the author of their salvation perfect through suffering." If we understand this connection, we will have a better understanding of our relationship to Christ and how he has called us to minister to others.

So think for a moment: how did suffering make Christ perfect? When he came to earth, wasn't he already perfect?

You see the connection illustrated in **Figure 6-1.** The left side pictures the life of Christ on earth. Christ had lived in eternity as the perfect Son of God, yet something else was needed before he could go to the cross as the perfect Lamb for sacrifice. His perfection needed to successfully endure the test of life in this fallen world. Christ needed to face sin and suffering without sinning. So at the end of his earthly life, how was Christ "made perfect"? He was now not only the perfect Son of God, but he had a perfection that had successfully endured the test of suffering. He now had demonstrated his righteousness on earth, and he had done so through suffering.

Notice, as you look at the picture, the direct analogy to his work in us. We are declared perfect in Christ (justification), but through the process of suffering, we actually do become holy (sanctification). We are being made perfect through the same process that Christ went through. The identity we share is:

- Brothers.
- Brothers in suffering.
- Brothers in suffering that leads to holiness.

This is also the identity we share with those we seek to love and help. Even with unbelievers, this shared brotherhood is our goal. We stand alongside each other. We are equals (brothers). We share the same experience (suffering). Our experience has the same goal (holiness). Let's consider how this identity should shape personal ministry:

It determines our posture in personal ministry. We do not stand above the people God calls us to serve. We stand alongside them as brothers, pointing them to the Father who is our source of help.

It determines the character of our ministry. Christ's humility in identifying with us in Hebrews 2 calls us to minister to others with a humble compassion (love). We are humble because we recognize that we too are people in the midst of God's process of change.

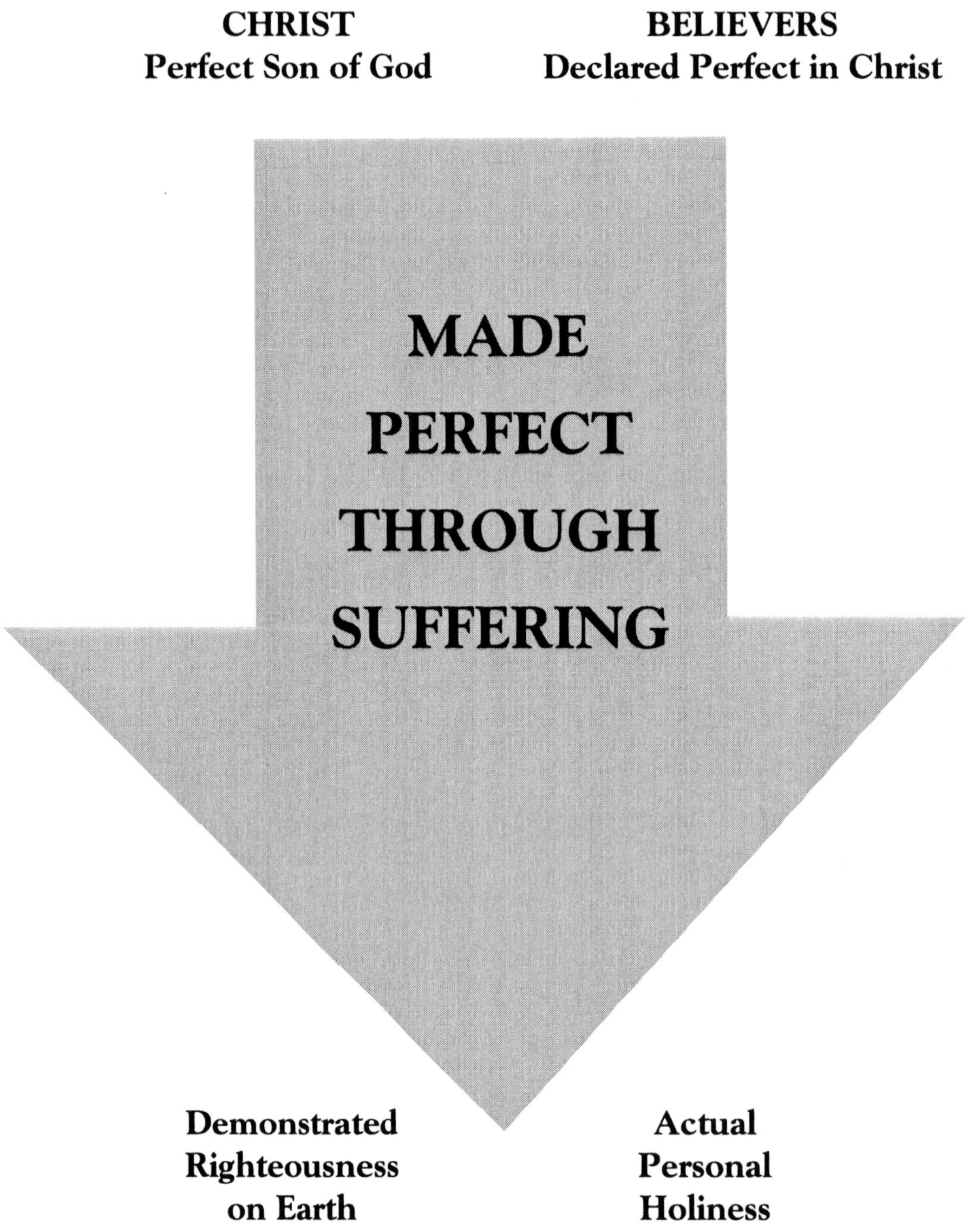

CHRIST
Perfect Son of God

BELIEVERS
Declared Perfect in Christ

MADE PERFECT THROUGH SUFFERING

Demonstrated Righteousness on Earth

Actual Personal Holiness

Figure 6-1. Fellow Sufferers with Christ (Hebrews 2:10-11).

And we are compassionate because we understand the realities of suffering that God uses to form us into his image.

It deals with the dependency issue. Often in personal ministry the person receiving help develops an unhealthy dependence on the person God is using in his life. Here it is clear that you — the helper — are not what the person needs. In fact, you are just like him — a person in need of God's ongoing work of change.

It redeems my experience. All of the experiences God has brought me through, all of the things he has done for me, and all the ways he has changed me give me stories to tell. These personal stories allow me to present God's truth with a flesh and blood realism. This clarifies the truths being presented and gives hope to the hearer. My life becomes a window through which the person can see the grace and glory of the Lord.

4. Accept with Agenda

Here again we follow the example of Christ's love for us. The amazing grace that causes Christ to accept me into his family is not a grace that says I am okay. In fact, it is clear that the reason God extends his gracious acceptance to me is that I am everything but okay. As you and I enter God's family, we are people in need of radical personal change. So God's acceptance is not a call to relax, but a call to work. We need to rest in his gift of grace, knowing that we do not have to earn acceptance with him. At the same time we need to realize that he calls us to participate in his life-long work of change.

It is wrong to approach a struggling brother or sister with a critical, condemning, self-righteous spirit. You must grant them the same grace and love that you received from God. At the same time, you do not want that offer of grace to be misunderstood. God's grace is always grace leading to change. Change is God's agenda in order that we would become partakers of his divine nature (**2 Peter 1:4**). As we seek to love people with the love of Christ, we must also hold before them God's call to change (**Titus 2:11-3:8**).

THE BIG QUESTION: Are you building relationships in which acceptance and a call to change are woven together?

CPR

Concepts

1. God ordains for us to suffer so that we would be qualified agents of his comfort and compassion.

2. God calls us to offer to others the same loving acceptance that he has given us. That acceptance always has change as its goal.

Personalized

1. Have I tended to hoard the comfort that God has given me?

2. Am I taking advantage of the opportunities God is giving me to comfort others with the comfort I have received from him?

3. Have I accepted God's call to participate in his process of lifelong change?

Related to others

1. I need to look for the sufferers God has placed in my path.

2. What stories in my own life could be used as examples of the hope and comfort God gives us in suffering?

3. Right now, where is God giving me the opportunity to offer grace leading to change to another person?

How to Tell Your Story
A Biblical Model
(2 Corinthians 1:3-11)

1. ***The Paradigm***: Viewing suffering redemptively.

    - God, the source of true compassion (v. 3).
    - God's comfort has ministry in view (v. 4).
    - God's purposes for us to share in Christ's suffering (v. 5).
    - Even our suffering does not belong to us, but to the Lord (v. 6).
    - The redemptive purpose in all of this is firm hope amid the harsh realities of a fallen world (v. 7).

2. ***The methodology***: Telling the stories of my struggle and the Lord's help.

    - Tell your story in a way that breaks down the misconception that you are essentially different from the person you are helping (v. 8).
    - Always tell a completed story. It needs to include a difficult situation, your struggle in the midst of it, and how God helped you (v. 8).
    - As you tell your story, be honest in describing your struggles and failures (v. 9).
    - Be discerning and purposeful as you tell the story. Limit the amount of "gory" detail. The situation is not the focus, but the God who met you in the middle of it (v. 9).

- Always tell your story in a way that makes God the key actor in the drama (v. 10).

- Tell your story with humility, admitting your continuing need for grace. Perhaps you will seek help (prayer) from the person to whom you are ministering (vv. 10, 11).

- Always state that the story makes it clear that you are not what this person needs—God is. At best, you are one of God's instruments, who shares a daily need for his mercy and grace (v. 9).

- The goal of your story should always be worship. All true hope and comfort are rooted in a recognition of and thankfulness for God, his character, and his help. True hope does not come because you try to say something that will somehow make the person feel better (v. 11).

3. ***Corollary passage*: 2 Corinthians 4:7-18.**

Helping Others Change
Make It Real

LESSON 6

In **2 Corinthians 1:3-7,** Paul makes it clear that our suffering and our experience of God's comfort have ministry in view. As I consider my own stories, I prepare myself to offer to others the same comfort I received from the Lord. I look back on my experiences not only to be thankful for what God has done, but to encourage others to rely on the grace of Christ as they suffer. So celebrate God's comfort as you look back, but don't just celebrate! Look for the ways God has equipped you to bring his comfort to others. Ask him, "Is there someone I know who needs this comfort right now?"

1. List three situations in which God ministered his comfort to you in the midst of difficulty, suffering, or trial.

2. List the things you learned from these situations about God's presence, power, grace, love, promises, provisions, etc.

3. In light of your ***Personal Ministry Opportunity***, write out one of your "stories" using the guide from **2 Corinthians 1:3-11.** Connect your story specifically to the person or group you have chosen as your focus. Pray for an opportunity to share it.

KNOW I: Getting to Know People; Discovering Where Change is Needed

DISCUSS HOMEWORK

REVIEW

1. Our hearts direct our lives, so God, in his redemptive love, is jealous for control of our hearts (Lessons 1-3).

2. God calls us to be his ambassadors, representing his message, methods, and character to those around us (Lesson 4).

3. Living as an ambassador means incarnating the ***LOVE*** of Christ, seeking to **KNOW** where change is needed in a person's life, being faithful to ***SPEAK*** the truth in love, and assisting people to ***DO*** what God has called them to do (Lessons 4-6).

In this lesson, we move to the second of the four elements of a biblical model of personal ministry (***KNOW***). Here again, Christ is our model. Like him, we need to enter the world of the people we

serve so that we can minister with the same sympathetic understanding we have received from him.

In this lesson, we will discuss ways in which our effectiveness as ambassadors is blunted when we don't know one another very well. We will learn to ask good questions that provide the information we need to minister to others in the places where change is really needed.

CONCEPTS AND OBJECTIVES

Concept: Wise people are not just people with the right answers, but people who ask the right questions. You cannot get to the right answers without asking the right questions.

Personalized: I need to ask good questions and avoid making assumptions about people that keep me from doing so.

Related to others: I will look for opportunities to ask questions that move me beyond casual relationships and provide insight as to where ministry is needed.

LESSON CONTENT

Have you ever thought you knew someone well, only to discover significant parts of his story that you did not know at all? Have you ever started to share a story from your own life and been interrupted by someone who said, "I know exactly what you mean!"—but clearly didn't? Right now, think of someone you believe you know very well. Try to identify some things about him or her that you don't know. Try to pinpoint the gaps in your understanding of his or her story.

This is what we will address in this lesson. We tend to live in terminally casual relationships. Yes, there are things that we know about each other (like who is married to whom, how many kids they have, who lives and works where, etc.). But the facts we know about people make us think that we know the human beings attached to those details. And because we assume that we know

the people around us, we don't ask them good questions. This keeps our relationships trapped in the casual and sets the stage for all kinds of potential misunderstandings between others and ourselves. Today we'll consider the importance of knowing people and gathering the data necessary to minister effectively to those around us.

Christ the Data Gatherer

Perhaps you've looked at the title of this section and thought, "Aren't you stretching things a bit?" Yet even in this area, Christ is our chief example. Turn in your Bibles to **Hebrews 4:14-16.** Let's examine the logic of this passage together.

In verse 16, the writer of Hebrews says that in the midst of our struggles we can come to Jesus with confidence, knowing that we will receive mercy and grace appropriate to our need. It is right, then, to ask, "Why can we be so confident as we come to Christ for help?" Verse 15 tells us. Christ is able to sympathize with our weaknesses. The author uses powerful words here. The word for sympathy used here literally means to be touched by what has touched someone else, or to be moved by what has moved someone else. This is more than pity, where you feel sorry for a person in a tough situation. This is understanding what it is like to be in that circumstance, coupled with a desire to help the person out.

The word for weaknesses is also very strong. It is almost untranslatable, but it is best understood as meaning "the human condition." The writer is saying that Jesus really does understand what it means to live in this fallen world. He understands all the things that push and pull us. He understands all the temptations we face. He understands how difficult and complicated our relationships are. He understands the limits of human strength and wisdom. He understands the difficult situations in which we find ourselves (disloyalty, betrayal, rejection, physical pain, aloneness, etc.). He understands the nature of families. Jesus has a complete understanding of our daily lives. He knows us!

How does Christ have such an accurate understanding of our existence? The passage clearly tells us with these words: "...we have one who has been tempted in every way, just as we are—yet was without sin" (v. 15). Jesus understands us because he entered our world. For thirty-three years Jesus lived on earth, gathering data about the nature of our experience in a fallen world. He was literally "tempted in every way, just as we are." Christ's experiences during those years between his birth and the cross made him a high priest who could sympathize with our weaknesses. Because he entered our world, his understanding is firsthand and complete.

Like Christ, we want to understand people so that we can serve them. Unlike Christ, we do not usually move in with people physically. However, by taking time to ask good questions and listen well, we can begin to understand how they are responding to the situations and relationships they face daily. Our hope is that this would give others confidence to seek us out, to share more of their true struggles, and find, through us, the help that the Lord can give.

The Problem of Assumptions

Because we speak the same language, share many of the same experiences, live in the same community, and often attend the same church, it is easy to assume that we know more about people than we actually do. When we simply assume a similarity of thought, desire, and experience, we don't ask the questions we need to ask. This leads us to make unvalidated assumptions about people, and may lead us to minister to people who exist only in our minds!

For personal ministry to be effective, it must be based on a rich base of information gathered by asking good questions. Assuming that you know what you need to know and failing to ask appropriate questions almost always leads to misunderstandings that blunt and divert personal ministry. The principle here is, "Don't assume, ask." Then you can be sure that what you have concluded is actually true.

To make sure that your conclusions are valid, there are three things you must regularly do:

Ask people to define their terms. Human language is messy. We all define even familiar words in very different ways.

Ask people to clarify what they mean with concrete, real life examples of the terms they have used.

Ask people to explain why they responded the way they did in the examples they have given you.

When I ask a person to define, clarify, and explain, I avoid the misunderstandings and false assumptions that can rob personal ministry of its effectiveness. Definition, clarification, and explanation are things I should ask for again and again.

Asking Good Questions

The primary way we get to know people is through the question and answer process. That makes it important to learn to ask good questions. Here are four principles to keep in mind.

1. ***Always ask open-ended questions — questions that cannot be answered with a "yes" or "no."*** Yes and no questions do not give us much information because we do not know the thoughts behind the answer. For example, if I ask if you have a good marriage and you answer, "Yes," what have I learned? I haven't learned much because I do not know your definition of a good marriage.

Notice that open-ended questions cannot be answered without the person disclosing how he is thinking, what he wants, and what he is doing.

2. ***Use a combination of survey and focused questions.*** Survey questions scan the various areas of a person's life, looking at the person as a whole. Survey questions reveal themes and patterns. For example, a woman's relational problem with her husband may also exist with her parents and her children. It is not, therefore, an isolated problem, but a theme in her life.

   Focused questions look intensively at one area of a person's life. Where survey questions scan widely, focused questions dig deeply into one area. Focused questions reveal roots and causes.

To get to know someone, we need to employ both kinds of questions. There are times when we need a wide-angle view, asking ourselves, "Does what I am seeing here exist elsewhere in this person's life?" We also need focused questions, asking ourselves, "What can I learn about what this person thinks, desires, and does by digging deeply into this one area of life?"

3. ***Always remember that certain kinds of questions reveal certain kinds of information.*** Ask yourself, "What do I need to know about this person to help him? What kind of question will uncover that information?"

There are essentially five classes of questions:

- **What?** questions are your most basic question. They uncover general information. ("What did you do?" "I talked to my wife.")

- **How?** questions reveal the way something was done. ("How did you talk to her?" "I yelled at her for fifteen minutes!")

- **Why?** questions uncover a person's purposes, desires, goals, or motivations. ("Why did you yell for so long?" "I wanted her to know how angry I was at what she had done.")

- **How often? Where?** questions. These questions reveal themes and patterns in a person's life. ("Where did this happen?" "At the supper table. Suppers are hard. We are both tired. We have young children. Meals are not relaxing. The evening meal always seems to be tense for us.")

- **When?** questions. When questions uncover the order of events. ("Tell me exactly when you began to yell during supper." "In the middle of the chaos my wife said, 'Well, how was your day?' She was obviously annoyed because I hadn't asked about hers. I said, 'Do you care or are you just being nasty?' She said, 'Well, you're the only one here with an interesting and important life, right?' At that point I blew up.")

Each class of question uncovers different information and thereby broadens or deepens your understanding of what took place (the situation), how the person interacted with it (the thoughts and motives of the heart), and what he did in response (behavior). You will use these questions whether you are focusing on one area or surveying a person's life.

4. ***Ask a progressive line of questions, in which each question is based on information uncovered in previous questions.*** There should be order and logic to the flow of questions. Each question should broaden or deepen your understanding of whatever is being considered. You accomplish this by always asking yourself, "What do I not know about what I have just heard?" This question challenges you not to make assumptions or fill in the gaps yourself.

THE BIG QUESTION: As you minister to others, do you ask good, biblical questions or is your ministry weakened by assumptions?

CPR

Concepts

1. Insightful people are not the people with the right answers but the ones who ask the right questions. You cannot arrive at the right answers without the right questions.

2. Christ is our example of entering a person's world, understanding what is there, and thus being able to fully sympathize and understand.

3. Relationships that are trapped in the casual don't lend themselves to fruitful personal ministry.

Personalized

1. I need to be interested in the lives of the people around me if I want opportunities to serve as an instrument of change.

2. I need to be committed to move beyond the casual at home, at work, in my neighborhood, and in the body of Christ.

3. I need to ask where I have missed ministry opportunities that God has given me because I did not know the person well enough to understand and respond.

Related to others

1. I need to be committed to asking good questions of people, not to satisfy my curiosity, but to fulfill my call as one of Christ's ambassadors.

2. I need to ask what I do not know about people that keeps me from effective personal ministry.

3. I want to be a sympathetic and understanding instrument in God's hands, one to whom people can come with confidence.

Helping Others Change
Make It Real

LESSON 7

Reflect on your ***Personal Ministry Opportunity*** in the following ways:

1. List the places where you have been tempted to make assumptions instead of asking questions you needed to ask.

2. Where do you have gaps in your information about this person/group and his/their world?

3. List some open-ended questions you could ask to get this information.

4. Pray for God's wisdom and discernment as you seek to understand this person or group.

KNOW II: Getting to Know People; Discovering Where Change is Needed

DISCUSS HOMEWORK

REVIEW

Jina is an attractive 17-year-old high school student who has always done well in school. Recently she has refused to get out of bed in the mornings and protested about going to school. She is spending an unusual amount of time in her room. Last night she sat through dinner with her head down. When her mother asked her what was wrong, she said she was too depressed to eat and ran out of the room. At that point, her mother called you.

1. What open-ended questions would you ask?

2. What survey questions would you ask?

3. What focused questions would you ask?

4. What different kinds of questions would you ask to uncover different kinds of information?

5. Ask a progressive line of questions in which each question is based on information from the previous question.

CONCEPTS AND OBJECTIVES

Concept: Personal ministry is not shaped by the facts you gather, but by the way you interpret those facts.

Personalized: I need to think in distinctively biblical ways about myself and the people God places in my path.

Related to others: One of the primary ways to function as an instrument of change is to help others think biblically about their situations and relationships, thoughts, motives, and behavior.

LESSON CONTENT

Have you ever had someone ask for your help with a problem and you simply didn't know what to say? Have you ever had someone ask, "What does the Bible say about 'x'?" and you didn't have an answer? Do you know that you never respond to life based on the facts of your experiences, but on your interpretation of those facts? Do you know that as you listen to others share their story, you are instinctively and actively making sense out of what you are hearing? Do you know that whatever you say in response will not be based on what they said, but on the sense that you made out of it?

Because we are always interpreting and because we have been called to be Christ's ambassadors, it is essential that we learn how to make biblical sense out of our lives and the lives of those around us. Only in this way can we know someone as God intends.

The Blind Leading the Blind

Have you ever noticed that we may spend hours preparing for a Sunday School class, a Bible study, or an elders' meeting, yet we will offer counsel to someone on the spur of the moment, with little or no preparation? (For example, your friend calls you in great distress. She was cleaning out her son's sock drawer and found a bag of marijuana. Without missing a beat, you begin to advise her on how to handle this very serious issue.) Because we do not take the time to think biblically about what others share with us, very often we are the blind leading the blind. As we seek to know and help people, we must always ask ourselves, "What principles, promises, perspectives, themes, and commands of Scripture speak to this person in this situation?" Our counsel will only be biblical if we have taken time to filter what we have heard through a sound biblical grid.

There is never a day when we do not advise and counsel one another. A wife may advise her husband as he is getting ready for work. A parent may coach a child on how to face a difficulty at school. A brother may help his sister talk through some problems with her friends. A boss may confront a worker. It may involve nothing more than what to order at the local diner, or it may be a serious discussion over the future of a marriage. But every day we influence one another. Every day we share our interpretations of life with one another and tell people what we think about their circumstances, relationships, and responses. The question is whether our "ministry" to one another is biblical. In all of this talk, are we asking ourselves what the Bible has to say about what we are discussing? If not, it is very easy for all of that advice-giving to be little more than the blind leading the blind.

Organizing the Information Biblically

Getting to know another person is like going around the house and collecting the laundry. Before long, you will have gathered a diverse pile of clothes, but they all must be sorted before you throw them in the washer! The same is true of getting to know another person. We don't talk about ourselves in organized categories. What we say comes out in a messy and chaotic way. We mix past history with present circumstances. We mix emotions right in with logical thoughts. We interpret the behavior of others when we talk about ourselves. We say things about God as we describe our circumstances. It all comes out as a messy pile of facts that need organization and interpretation.

One way to promote godly change in others is to learn how to think about what they say in an organized, biblical way. We can then help them interpret their lives and make changes that reflect God's truth. This lesson will teach you how to do that.

Let's say that John's wife Greta asks to talk with you. When you meet, she says that she is concerned about her husband. John has an increasingly short fuse. He yells at her and the children at the drop of a hat. He is critical and demanding. He is spending more time at work and most of his home time is spent on the computer. When Greta asks John what is wrong, he just says that life stinks. Greta says that John's dad was a negative guy who always thought that people were out to get him. John was not like that when she married him, but Greta is afraid he is turning into his father. When Greta asks John how she can help him, all he says is, "Just give me a little space so I can breathe."

Now turn to **Figure 8-1.** This is a simple tool to help you sort the information you receive as you get to know someone. Ask yourself the four questions to organize what he tells you.

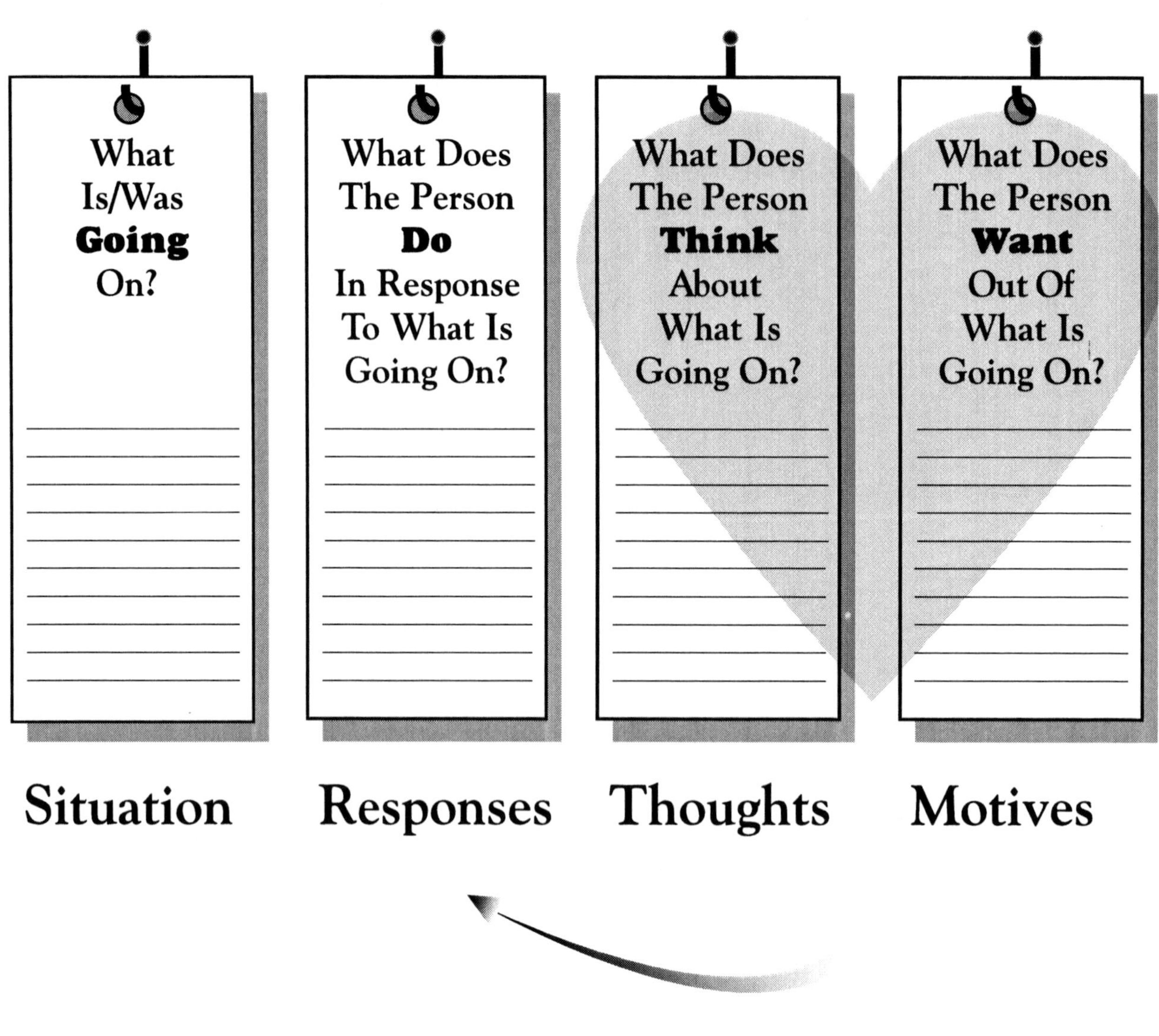

Figure 8-1. Knowing a Person Biblically.

1. ***The Situation.*** (What is going on?) Here I place all the information that describes what the person's world is like. I must include both past and present. (In the past, John was raised by a negative, cynical father. In the present, he is an increasingly angry, critical, distant husband.)

2. ***The Responses.*** (What does the person do in response to what is going on?) Here I include facts that describe the person's behavior. (John is yelling at his family, spending more time at work, and staying on the computer at home.)

3. ***The Thoughts.*** (What does the person think about what is going on?) Include information on how he has been interpreting his world. ("Life stinks.")

4. ***The Motives.*** (What does the person want out of, or in the midst of, what is going on?) Include what you know about the person's desires, goals, purposes, treasures, motives, values, and idols. What does he live for? What really rules his heart? ("Just give me space so I can breathe.")

These four categories (Situation, Responses, Thoughts, Motives), provide four hooks to organize the information I have gathered.

Using the Hooks

1. ***The Situation.*** For personal ministry to be effective, I must understand the person's everyday world. What pressures, opportunities, responsibilities, and temptations does she face every day? Who are the significant people in her life, and what are they doing? What circumstances does she face every day? What do I know about her past (the people and circumstances then)? From all this information I want to extract the things that will help me understand her world. So I ask myself, "What is (was) going on?" I hang all of the situational information on this hook.

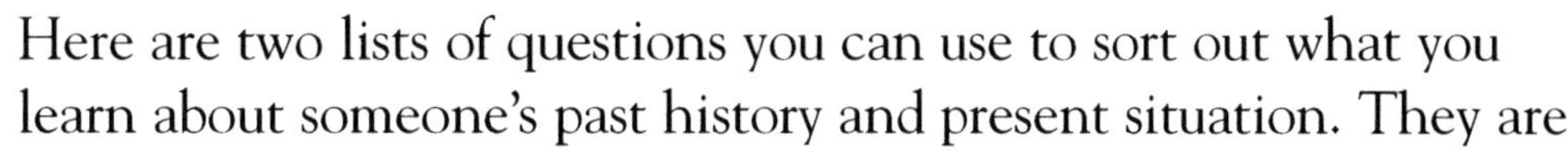

Here are two lists of questions you can use to sort out what you learn about someone's past history and present situation. They are not meant to be exhaustive lists, but "pump-primers" to give you a sense of the kinds of things to listen for.

Historical

- Family of origin. What do I know about this person's childhood?

- Dynamic events. What major events (death in the family, divorce, crippling accident, etc.) shaped or influenced this person's life?

- Significant relationships. Outside the home, who were the people of influence in this person's life (coach, relative, friend, teacher, pastor, etc.)?

- Significant experiences. These are not the crisis events, but the long-term experiences that shaped the person's life (major family move, going to college, coming to Christ).

Remember, this list is not exhaustive. It simply suggests things that may be important to understand about the person's past.

Present

- The life context. These are all the situations and relationships that the person faces every day (pressures, opportunities, responsibilities, temptations, etc.).

- Significant relationships. Who are the people of influence in this person's life today?

- Present family. What have I learned about the family in which this person is currently living?

- Presenting problem. How does the person describe her struggle? What does she say is wrong?

The goal here is to get know this person in her world. I need to know the details of her world because my call, as Christ's ambassador, is to represent him (in his message, methods, character) in that context. My calling is to build a bridge of understanding from the Word of God to the details of her world so that she can understand what God has promised her and called her to do. So, I begin by pulling out of my pile of information everything I have learned about this person's situation. I place it under the question, "What is going on?"

2. ***The Responses.*** Here my focus is on the person's behavior. I know she has been acting, reacting, and responding. I want to collect all the information that describes what this person does in response to what is going on in her world. As I do this, I am looking for themes and patterns. What are the typical ways she responds to situations and people? These themes and patterns will give me some idea of what is going on in her heart. (Certain roots in the heart produce certain fruit in the person's life.) So, I take out any information that describes this person's behavior and place it under the question, "What does this person do in response to what is going on?"

3. ***The Thoughts.*** Here we are considering the "heart" that directs the person's behavior. We know that this person is a meaning maker; that is, she is always trying to make sense out of her life. We know that this person doesn't respond just to the facts of her life, but to her interpretation of those facts. We know that lasting change always takes place through the pathway of the heart. So, if I am going to be an instrument of change, it is vital to know how this person is thinking. There is a very real possibility that change will need to begin here.

Remember that the thoughts of the heart precede and determine our activity. Turn to **Numbers 11.** This passage gives us a window on the importance of our thoughts about a particular situation and how those thoughts shape our responses.

Israel is in the wilderness and God is sending manna for food. The Israelites become dissatisfied and begin craving other food. God finally responds to their complaint by sending quail, three feet deep, for as far as you could walk in a day! Let's look at the thinking of the children of Israel as they responded to their situation.

- They had a distorted view of the **past**. If you read the description of Egypt in verses 4 and 5, it sounds more like a restaurant than a place of suffering, slavery, and death! For 420 years Israel had prayed to be liberated from this place. Now they were longing for it. Our perspective on our past is often shockingly selective.

- They had a distorted view of the **present**. The average Israelite, standing at the door of his tent and seeing manna morning after morning, thought of this situation as an awful trial. Yet they were experiencing one of the clearest indications of God's covenant faithfulness that they had ever seen. Because he had promised to sustain them when they could not produce food themselves, God harnessed the forces of nature to provide for his people. This is such a clear demonstration of his love that Jesus takes "Manna" as one of his names. He declares that he is the bread that has come down from heaven, the only bread that can truly satisfy (**John 6: 32-35**). The Israelites should have looked at the manna each morning and thought, "How could God love us enough to do this miraculous thing day after day?"

- They had a distorted view of **self**. Moses is our example here. His prayer in verses 10-15 reveals that he had a completely distorted perspective on who he is and what he has been called to do. He thought it was his job to "carry" Israel. He was so convinced that he had been given an impossible job to do that he asked God to take his life! There was clear evidence in the cloud by day, the pillar of fire by night, and the manna every morning that it was God who was guiding and sustaining his people. Moses' view of himself and his job could not have been more distorted.

- They had a distorted view of **God**. If you combine Israel's complaints against God with Moses' view of God (vv.21, 22), you get a picture of how distorted Israel's functional theology actually was. As Israel saw it, God was distant and uncaring. He was weak and small. He was untrustworthy. He was not a god to whom you would entrust your life and your future.

- They had a distorted view of the **future**. According to the thinking of the Israelites, what options did they have? On the one hand, they could go back to Egypt where good food was available, but where they would once again be subjected to slavery, suffering, and death. Or, they could entrust themselves to a god who was distant, uncaring, untrustworthy, and weak. This is functional hopelessness — neither situation seems attractive or workable. The future appears to give Israel no reason for hope and because of that, no reason to continue.

If I have a distorted view of the past, present, myself, God, and the future, there is no way that I will respond properly to what God has placed on my plate. We need to look for the seeds of wrong behavior in a person's distorted and unbiblical thought. Because of this, it is vital to organize all of the facts that describe how this person thinks about life. We place all of that information under the question, "What does this person think about what is going on?"

4. ***The Motives.*** We know that there is always something or someone ruling our hearts. We know that whatever rules our hearts will control our behavior. We know that our desires battle for control within our hearts. We know that we all live for certain treasures. We know that behind every action, reaction, or response are desires, motives, goals, and purposes. We know that we quickly exchange worship and service for the Creator for worship and service of the created thing. So, it is very important to collect all the information that describes what this person truly wants, what desires really rule her heart, or what idols have taken control. Since our behavior is our attempt to get what is important to us from people and situations, real change will always include the

motives of the heart. Because of this, we must be able to identify the person's motives. We place all of this information under the question, "What does this person want out of (or in the midst of) what is going on?"

Once we have organized the information the person has given us, it is no longer a chaotic pile of facts. It is now in categories that help the information to speak to us. This should help us see where change needs to take place in this person's life.

An Opportunity to Use the Tool

At the end of the lesson you will see a one-page case study entitled "Sharon." Let's attempt to use the hook illustration to organize the information given there.

THE BIG QUESTION: In personal ministry, do you take time to organize information in a way that helps you interpret it biblically?

CPR

Concepts

1. Personal ministry is not shaped by the facts you gather, but by the way you interpret those facts.

2. Interpreting information biblically begins with organizing the material under biblical categories.

Personalized

1. I need to be aware that I never live based on the facts of my experience, but on how I interpret those facts.

2. Since I am always interpreting, I need to be aware of how my reactions to others are shaped by the sense I have made out of their choices, behavior, and words.

3. I must be committed to making Scripture my primary tool for interpreting life.

Related to others

1. One of the primary ways I will function as God's instrument of change is to help those around me to think about their lives in a distinctively biblical way.

2. As I get to know people, I need to take the time necessary to let biblical categories sort out the information they give me.

3. As I listen to people tell their stories, I need to ask, "What does the Bible say about what I am hearing?"

SHARON

Sharon approached me after our Sunday service. She said that her marriage was a "mess" and that we needed to talk "immediately." I told her that it sounded too important to squeeze into a few minutes. I set a time to meet with Sharon and asked her to invite her husband. Sharon came alone and told her story emotionally and in great detail. She said that her husband Ed was unwilling to come. He told her that either she "got her act together" or he was "out of here."

Sharon told of an increasingly tense relationship. She spoke of the fact that she and Ed were no longer sleeping in the same room or going anywhere together. They had separate bank accounts and recently had agreed it was "best" to eat supper separately. Their two young children took turns eating with each parent.

Even before their marriage they had experienced problems in communication. Ed felt that Sharon was always trying to control him and his decisions. Sharon felt that Ed never really paid attention to her viewpoint unless she "made it real clear." Yet Ed always said that Sharon was the most beautiful woman in the world and Sharon said that Ed was the best thing that had ever happened to her.

Ed was a "mover and shaker" with an ever-expanding import business, and Sharon enjoyed being with "people that matter." Sharon had lived in foster homes all her life, never really knowing her real parents. Ed was raised in a typical working class neighborhood in the city.

Sharon said that Ed had been saying for years that she was slowly destroying his manhood. Sharon confessed to having two affairs during the marriage. She said that Ed was very angry and she appeared to be the same.

Sharon made her agenda for counseling very clear when we first talked by saying, "I am not here to work on me. I think I am okay. I am here because my marriage is in trouble. Do you think you can get my husband to talk to you? He's the one who needs help!"

Helping Others Change
Make It Real

LESSON 8

In light of your ***Personal Ministry Opportunity***, use the following categories and questions to organize the information you have gathered about your person or group. Refer to the Sharon case study as an example.

1. ***Situation.*** List everything you can find about the person's circumstances.

2. ***Response.*** List everything you can that characterizes the person's responses to circumstances.

3. ***Thoughts***. List everything you can that describes the way the person thinks about his situation. How is he thinking about himself, God, change, etc?

4. ***Motives.*** List everything you can that describes what the person wants out of (or in the midst of) the situation.

5. Pray specifically for God's wisdom and discernment as you try to understand this person.

SPEAK I: Speaking the Truth in Love

DISCUSS HOMEWORK

REVIEW

CONCEPTS AND OBJECTIVES

Concepts: Confrontation needs to be rooted in the comfort and call of the gospel.

Personalized: I must examine my life. Do the promises, provisions, and obligations of the gospel shape my living?

Related to others: As I seek to help others examine themselves in the mirror of God's Word, I must be committed to encouraging and comforting them with the gospel.

LESSON CONTENT

Rebuke is the word the Bible uses for bringing truth to where change is needed, yet most of us don't have positive reactions when we hear this word. For example, if I called you one night and told you that I would like to come over the next morning to rebuke you, how would you respond? Would you run to your friend and say, "The most wonderful thing is going to happen to me tomorrow! ______________ is coming over to rebuke me. It has been so long since I've been rebuked. I just can't wait!" It's not likely that this would be your reaction. When we think of rebuke, we often think of a tense moment, of harsh words, red faces, ultimatums, and threats. We don't think of something that is an act of patient and committed love. So it is important for us to consider what a biblical model of rebuke looks like. We need to know what "speaking the truth in love" is all about. This is the focus of this lesson.

The Process of Confrontation

As we consider bringing truth to where change is needed, perhaps the best way to begin is to talk about our goals, the results that should motivate us when we speak. **2 Corinthians 5:20** is very helpful here. It reminds us that we must approach truth-speaking in personal ministry as God's representatives. What should motivate us is not our opinion, our anger, or our impatience. What should motivate us is God's desire to make his appeal to that person through us! Think about that for a moment. Almighty God has actually chosen to say important, life-changing things through us! In moments of biblical rebuke, our opinion doesn't make any difference. The only thing that counts is God's perspective as revealed in his Word. As God's representative, I must be careful not to combine what God has said with what I've always wanted to say.

In a rebuke, I want to incarnate the love of Christ by helping a person to see himself in the mirror of God's Word, and calling him to accept responsibility for sins of his heart and behavior.

If I have this as my goal, the process will look like the following:

1. ***Start with yourself.*** If I am going to speak as an ambassador, I affirm that biblical truth-speaking always begins with dealing with my own heart. I need to confess and forsake all the wrong thoughts and motives (anger, bitterness, thoughts of vengeance, a spirit of condemnation, etc.) that would stand in the way of what the Lord wants to do through me. And I must ask God to provide the love, courage, patience, and wisdom that I will need to represent him well. This step of personal preparation is often neglected in moments of confrontation. The result is that the rebuke is not effective, not only because the receiver was unwilling, but also because the representative was unprepared. If I do not start with my own heart I will tend to:

- Turn moments of ministry into moments of anger.
- Personalize things that are not personal.
- Be adversarial in my approach.
- Confuse my opinion with God's will.
- Settle for quick solutions that do not address the heart.

2. ***Understand why people need to be confronted.*** After our personal preparation, we can consider the goals we should have in view. The best way to do this is to ask the question, "Why do people need to be confronted?" The answers will direct us toward the proper set of goals. People need to be confronted because of:

1. The deceitfulness of sin. Sin blinds our hearts **(Hebrews 3:12,13)**.
2. Wrong and unbiblical thinking **(Numbers 11, Psalm 73)**.
3. Emotional thinking. We are all aware that we don't do our best thinking in times of great emotion. We will often be ministering to people who are in the midst of situations that are emotionally volatile.

4. My view of life (God, self, others, the solution, etc.) tends to be strengthened by my experiences. Because I am the one interpreting my experiences, my conclusions tend to be reinforced with each new situation. What I need is an intervention of truth to confront and correct my thinking.

3. ***Speak with God's goals in view.*** Our goals for rebuke must be equal to these challenges. Two goals together meet the standard. The first is that in confrontation, I would be used as one of God's instruments of seeing in the life of another. Yes, we do tend to be blind, and we do tend to be more aware of where others need to change and grow than we are of ourselves. So the goal of truth-speaking is to help people clearly see themselves in the mirror of God's Word. I am not there to help them see what I see, but what God sees. Because of this, it is the Word of God, and not my personal opinion, that I will hold before them.

The second goal of confrontation is to be used of God as an agent of repentance. The biblical definition of repentance is a change of heart that leads to a change in the direction of my life. True repentance always begins with the heart. Turn to **Joel 2:12,13,** which captures this for us. Joel talks not of rending the garments (the external behavior of remorse), but of rending the heart (heartfelt remorse for my sin accompanied by a desire to change). This is our goal, not to pressure and coerce people into changes in behavior, but to encourage heart change that impacts the person's response to life. Repentance literally means to turn and go in the other direction. This turning must begin with the heart.

So, as I try to speak truth into this person's life, I am not trying to advance my own opinion. Rather, I want to function as an instrument of seeing. I am not seeking simply to coerce the person into altering his behavior. Rather, my goal is that through the things I say ***(message),*** the way I say them ***(methods),*** and the attitudes I express ***(character),*** God will change the heart of this person.

Don't Leave the Gospel at the Door

A mistake we often make as we seek to lead someone to repentance is to emphasize the law over the gospel. Yet Paul says **(Romans 2:4)** that it is God's kindness (goodness) that leads us to repentance. He also says **(2 Corinthians 5:14)** that it is the love of Christ that compels us to no longer live for ourselves, but for him. It is the grace of the gospel that turns our hearts, because the gospel is God's magnificent promise of forgiveness in Christ Jesus. This is what draws us out of hiding into the light of truth, where true confession and repentance will take place.

As we confront people, we need to remind them of their identity in Christ **(2 Peter 1:3-9; 1 John 3:1-3)**. We need to remind them of God's promise of forgiveness **(1 John 1:5-10)**, and the amazing gift of the indwelling Holy Spirit **(Ephesians 3:20)**, who gives us the strength to obey. These truths give believers the courage to examine their hearts, confess their sin, and turn to Christ. If we are speaking as agents of repentance, it is not enough to come armed with the law. We must come armed with the gospel as well.

Romans 8:1-17 is helpful here because Paul captures the two sides of the gospel. Paul begins by alerting us to the comfort of the gospel (vv. 1-11). He points to two powerful redemptive realities. First, the work of the Lord Jesus Christ has removed the sentence of condemnation that was on my head because of my sin. Jesus paid the penalty for my sin. As I come to God in confession, I do not need to fear his wrath and rejection. Because Christ met the requirements of the law and went to the cross as an acceptable sin offering, I do not face condemnation! As we hold the mirror of the Word in front of people, helping them to see the presence and gravity of their sin, it is very important that we also comfort them with the fact that the work of Christ has satisfied God's anger. As I come to him, I can be confident that he will forgive.

The gospel also comforts us with the Holy Spirit, who lives within every believer. Before my salvation, I was controlled by the thoughts and desires of the sinful nature. I was not able to live as God has ordained. But now God lives inside me! I am no longer controlled by the sinful nature. I no longer have to live as a slave

to its passions and desires. The Holy Spirit now controls me. Paul says that the Holy Spirit gives life to my mortal body. What does this mean? It means that I am now dead to the controlling power of sin and alive for the purpose of obedience. God lives within me. I can follow him in simple acts of obedience amid life's daily situations and relationships. I do not have to live as if I am still a slave to sin. No, the Spirit has come to give me life, power, and the desire and ability to obey.

As we call people to own and confess their need before God, we must root our loving words of confrontation in the soil of the gospel. Condemnation has been removed. Forgiveness has been granted. The Holy Spirit lives inside us. We have power to obey. These truths give people the confidence they need to come out of hiding and confess their sin. And they give people the confidence that as they turn to a new way of living, they will have God's strength to do what he calls them to do.

But this is not all that Paul says about the gospel. Paul says that the gospel is not only a comfort, it is also a call. The call of the gospel is summarized by Paul in **Romans 8:12-17**. Paul uses the word obligation to define what the gospel calls us to. He essentially says that the ongoing work of God in the believer's life is to eradicate sin ("put to death the misdeeds of the body"). As a believer, I am obligated to participate in the Holy Spirit's search-and-destroy mission. I must not live "according to the sinful nature" any longer. I must accept my sonship, realizing that true sons of God are those who are "led by the Spirit," and not by the sinful nature.

Here is what we are seeking to accomplish as we root our truth-speaking in the gospel. Our goal is that the heart would be changed by the work of Christ that the gospel declares. First, our goal is that the gospel promises of forgiveness and power would give people real

hope of change. Second, our goal is that the call of the gospel would cause people to accept responsibility for their sin and to accept God's call to obey. The heart that has embraced both the hope (comfort) and the obligation (call) is now ready to receive words of confrontation. Now a person can see the gravity of his sin and the grandeur of God's call to obey in light of gospel truths. He is now ready to really live as a true child of God, as someone who is honest about himself and ready to follow God in daily acts of faith and obedience.

THE BIG QUESTION: Is the gospel central when you speak the truth to someone?

CPR

Concepts

1. The purpose of confrontation is twofold: to help people to see what God wants them to see and to lead them to repentance.

2. As I speak truth to people, I must not only bring the law to them, but the gospel as well.

3. It is the hope of Christ's forgiveness and the promise of his presence that draws us out of hiding toward confession and repentance.

Personalized

1. I must ask myself, "Do I confront others as an ambassador or do I tend to advance my own opinion?"

2. Am I zealous to comfort and encourage people with the gospel?

3. Is my life shaped and directed by the comfort and the call of the gospel?

Related to others

1. Do I look for opportunities to motivate people with the truths of the gospel?

2. Do I look for opportunities to function as one of God's instruments of seeing?

3. In moments of confrontation, do I want people to agree with me or turn to God?

Helping Others Change
Make It Real

LESSON 9

In light of your ***Personal Ministry Opportunity***, answer the following questions.

1. Think of a time in your life (1) when you were rebuked and (2) you had to rebuke someone else. How well did these encounters fulfill godly goals? Now apply this to your ***Personal Ministry Opportunity***. Have you begun with yourself? Are you moving towards the other person with a proper understanding of why he or she needs rebuke? Are you moving towards him with proper goals—to be an instrument of sight or an agent of repentance? Or are you going with ungodly motives: revenge, the desire to prove that you are right and he is wrong, etc.? Pray consistently for love, honesty, and humility.

2. What do you dislike most about confrontation? How can a gospel perspective, as both a comfort and a call, help you move toward the person you have chosen as your ministry focus? Where do you need compassion and courage, honesty and humility, encouragement and candor?

3. Study three of the gospel passages that your group shared during this lesson. Write down the specific comforts and provisions that they offer the child of God. How can you use them to encourage the person you need to confront?

SPEAK II: Speaking the Truth in Love

DISCUSS HOMEWORK

REVIEW

In Lesson 9 we focused on the importance of confrontation being rooted in the gospel. It is the comfort of the gospel that draws us out of hiding and brings us to the Lord with humble words of confession and obedient acts of repentance. It is the call of the gospel that causes us to be serious about sin and to faithfully participate as God works to remove it from our lives. If a person is going to be helped by the truth that is spoken to him, he must embrace both the hope and the obligation of the gospel.

We also examined the goal of confrontation. We do not speak the truth to advance our own opinions or to say things we have always wanted to say. Rather, to confront is to serve as an ambassador, communicating God's truth to someone. It is motivated by two goals:

- To serve as an instrument of seeing in this person's life. My hope is that my words would help this person see himself in the perfect mirror of God's Word.

- To be an agent of true repentance (a radical change of heart that leads to a radical change in the life).

In this lesson we will examine the progressive steps of confrontation and consider what the process should look like.

CONCEPTS AND OBJECTIVES

Concept: The progressive steps of confrontation are: consideration, confession, commitment, and change.

Personalized: I must be committed to a "put off" (consideration, confession) and "put on" (commitment, change) personal lifestyle.

Related to others: I must be committed to a process of speaking truth to others that encourages lasting change.

LESSON CONTENT

We all confront one another every day. A mom goes to wake her daughter for school and confronts her about the condition of her room. A brother confronts his sister, who took something from his room without permission. A wife confronts her husband about his distance and busyness. A neighbor confronts her neighbor about the way he spoke to her children. A pastor confronts a wayward man in his congregation. Driver confronts driver in traffic. A consumer confronts a store manager about his deceptive advertising. A married child confronts his mother about her interference in his marriage. Confrontation is a much more regular part of our daily lives than we often think.

The question in the midst of all this confrontation is, *Whose agenda are we following?* Are we confronting others like mini-kings, communicating our opinion and trying to get people to do what would please us? Or are we confronting as ambassadors, helping

others see themselves clearly in the mirror of God's Word, leading them to real repentance of the heart? This is the focus of this lesson. We want to examine the steps of biblical confrontation (confronting as ambassador of Christ).

Progressive Steps of Confrontation

If we want to do more than read people a list of charges from Scripture or tell them what we think of them, we must speak the truth with a clear sense of direction. If our goal is to function as instruments of seeing and agents of repentance, there are four specific steps to the process.

Let's say that you are friends with both Sally and Jim. Sally has expressed concern to you that Jim has begun to do things that are unbecoming to a Christian. He admits to cheating on his hours at work and to taking office supplies. He has been going to clubs that Sally thinks would make any Christian uncomfortable. Jim also reports a deteriorating relationship with his roommate, and Sally has been hurt that things she told Jim in confidence have been shared with you. She has tried to talk to Jim about his relationship with God. He has told you both that he is "discouraged with God" right now. He is thinking about changing churches or even moving away. You are concerned for Jim, know him well, and have a relationship of mutual trust. You decide to talk with him.

1. ***Consideration.*** The question to ask here is, "What does this person need to see (about himself, God, others, life, truth, change, etc.) that he does not now see, and how can I help him see it?" Often when people tell their story, they are not in it! Their account focuses on the toughness of the situation and the attitudes and behavior of others. Our goal is to encourage the person to look at his behavior and to examine his heart. We want to break through the walls of spiritual blindness and help a person to see himself, his relationships, and his circumstances with biblical eyes. To accomplish this

goal, there are five questions that we should regularly ask. The order is important because it teaches us to think biblically about why we do the things we do.

- ***What was going on?*** This question gives the person an opportunity to tell you what was happening around him. This information is important for him because you want the person to see that these things did not cause him to do what he did. It is important for you because you need to understand his world in order to speak truth into it. Do not assume that you know the details of a person's situation!

- ***What were you thinking and feeling as it was going on?*** This question immediately directs the person to examine his heart. In asking this question, we are teaching the person to be aware that the heart is always interacting with what is going on. We never leave our hearts at the door.

- ***What did you do in response?*** Again, notice the order of the questions. It reflects the fact that our behavior is not shaped by the facts of our situations and relationships, but by our hearts' response to those facts. In asking this question at this time, we are asking the person to admit that his behavior was not forced upon him by the situation ("It was the only thing I could do!") or by others ("She made me angry!"). It was shaped by what is in his heart.

- ***Why did you do it?*** What were you seeking to accomplish? If the second question uncovers thoughts, then this question reveals motives. In asking this question, we are teaching the person that the heart is always serving something. Our behavior is always directed by a functional worship and service for the Creator or for the creation **(Romans 1:25)**. Here the person is asked to consider how his behavior is his attempt to get what is important to him. Our behavior is always an expression of the purposes, desires, motives, treasures, lusts, or idols of the heart. Notice that questions 2 and 4 connect behavior to the thoughts and motives of the heart **(Hebrews 4:12)**. The order forces the person to

consider how his behavior is a logical expression of how his heart thinks and what his heart wants.

- ***What was the result?*** This question not only seeks to uncover consequences **(Galatians 6:7)**, but the way these consequences are a direct result of the thoughts and motives of the heart. The seeds planted in the heart grow into a full harvest of fruit in the person's situations and relationships. We are all quite skilled at denying our own harvest. ("If you had these kids, you'd yell too!" "I didn't really hear what you said." "He just pushes my buttons!") So it is important to get people to examine the fruit in their life in terms of their hearts. You want to lead people to "own" their own harvest. This happens when people are willing to look at themselves in the only mirror that is truly accurate, the Word of God.

2. ***Confession.*** This is the next logical step in the process. If people have looked at themselves in the mirror of Scripture, they should have identified sins of heart and behavior that need to be confessed. The problem is that sinners find confession difficult. It is more natural for us to deny, recast history, explain away, accuse, blame, defend, and hide. A person's confession needs to be concrete and specific, and not weakened by "if onlys." It is equally important that you do not confess for the person, but that you lead him to speak his own words of confession to the Lord. Further, he needs to be encouraged to confess horizontally, that is, to all of the people who have been affected by his sin.

   Don't assume confession! At appropriate times call the person to confession; ask him to pray, admit his sin, and seek God's forgiveness.

3. ***Commitment.*** The question to ask yourself here is, "Specifically, where is God calling this person to radical new ways of living?" To what new ways of thinking is God calling him? What new biblical desires would God want to control his heart? To what new responses is God calling him? In what new ways is God calling him to serve and love others? What things should he stop doing? What new things should he start doing? What steps of correction and restitution is God calling him to make? What new habits need to be inserted into his daily routine? Is the person committed to these things?

4. ***Change.*** It is easy to assume that change has taken place because the person has gained personal insight and made new commitments. But that would be a mistake. Change hasn't taken place until change has taken place! The insights and commitments need to be applied daily in a person's life circumstances and relationships. Commitment is the "what" and change is the "how."

   How will a husband begin to express servant love for his wife when he comes home from work? How will a son demonstrate a new honor and respect for his parents? In what ways can a man serve instead of control? How will a woman go about restoring a broken relationship? How will a man make changes in his slavery to his career? What new habits will a distant father insert into his daily routine so that he can more faithfully and lovingly parent his children? Change involves applying new commitments to the situations and relationships of daily living.

If we want our words to be instruments of change in moments of confrontation, we need a sense of direction. These four steps provide a roadmap for us:

1. ***Consideration.*** What does God want the person to see?
2. ***Confession.*** What does God want the person to admit and confess?

3. ***Commitment.*** To what new ways of living is God calling this person?
4. ***Change.*** How should these new commitments be applied to daily living?

Learn to Confront Biblically

We need to get away from a "reading the person the riot act" style of confrontation. In this style, the receiver is essentially silent while the confronter lays out a list of "charges" and calls for a response. In Scripture, the more common style of confrontation is interaction. The confronter stands alongside the person, helping him to see, telling stories, asking questions, drawing out answers, and then calling for a response. The confrontation has much more of a conversational structure. The primary example of this kind of confrontation is Christ and his parables. (See **Luke 7:36-50; 14:1-14.**) Christ speaks so that people might see, and in seeing, might confess, and in confessing, might turn. He confronts powerful attitudes, beliefs, and actions, yet the parables have a very different feel from our often tense moments of confrontation.

The principle here is, *Start with interaction.* Interactive confrontation includes:

- ***Two-way communication.*** If you want to be an instrument of seeing, the person being confronted must be invited to talk. You need to know that she has seen and understood what you are pointing out; that she has owned what needs to be admitted and confessed; that she is committed to new ways of living; and that she understands how change needs to be made. Feedback is vital.

- ***Use of metaphor*** (example: God is a rock, fortress, sun, shield, door, light, etc.). Here you are searching for things in a person's life that illustrate truth. (Reflect on the ministry of Christ and his use of common things to communicate uncommon truths.)

What do you know about this person's background, job, interests, experiences, etc., that would provide metaphors for you to use? The metaphor can be a single comparison ("He is a whirlwind") or an extended story (the parables of Christ).

- ***Self-confronting statements.*** Here you are encouraging the person to make connections between the examples you have used and his own life. Don't rush to make those connections for him! It is vital that his heart embraces what God is showing him and that, without pressure, he is ready to confess and turn from sin.

- ***Summary.*** Here you are drawing together all that you think God wants to teach the person and calling him to respond with heartfelt commitment. When you summarize, make sure that the issues are clear and that you don't assume a person's agreement. Ask for commitment.

In moments of confrontation, it is always important to start with interaction. But there are times when you are called to minister to a person who is stubborn, rebellious, and proud. Such people (the Pharisees, for example) will not participate in the give-and-take of interactive confrontation. They need to hear God's will pronounced and exhorted to respond. This style of confrontation, declaration, is what we most often associate with confrontation, but it should be reserved for those who refuse to do the self-examination that interactive confrontation requires. We should always begin with interaction (engaging a person in heartfelt self-examination) and only move to declaration ("Thus says the Lord," with a call to repent) when interaction is ineffective. (See **Matthew 23:13-39; Amos 6; 2 Samuel 12:1-14**).

THE BIG QUESTION: What does it look like to confront someone biblically?

CPR

Concepts

1. The goal of confrontation is lasting change in a person's heart and life.
2. The progressive steps of confrontation are: consideration, confession, commitment, and change.
3. If the goals of confrontation are to help a person to see his sin and to repent, then it is essential that the confrontation be interactive.

Personalized

1. I must be committed to a process of truth-speaking that results in lasting heart change.
2. I must follow the example of Christ as I speak truth and seek to give sight to those around me.
3. I must ask myself, Where is God seeking to help me see and lead me to repentance?

Related to others

1. I must patiently lead people through the steps of confrontation.
2. I must learn to ask good, heart-revealing questions.
3. I must learn to find metaphors in others' lives that help them to see truth.

Helping Others Change
Make It Real

LESSON 10

Answer the following questions in light of your ***Personal Ministry Opportunity***.

1. How will the progressive steps of confrontation help your confrontation to be godly?

    a. What does the person need to consider? How will you help him see what he needs to see?

    b. What things does he need to confess? How will you assist him in godly confession?

c. What commitments does the person need to make? How can you help them be specific and concrete?

d. What practical changes need to take place? How will you assist the person to be specific so that he can determine whether or not real change has happened?

2. How will you best confront the person you have chosen for your ***Personal Ministry Opportunity***? Be creative as you study the multiple ways that confrontation can take place: two-way communication, use of metaphor, self-confrontation, summary.

3. How well have you done the confrontation described in Questions 1 and 2? What have you typically done? Where do you need to change? Do you need to confess sinful and unwise behavior to the person you have chosen for your ***Personal Ministry Opportunity***?

4. Pray honestly and faithfully for God's work in your heart in these areas.

DO I: Applying Change to Everyday Life

DISCUSS HOMEWORK

REVIEW

In Lesson 1 we learned that:
To be human is to need truth outside of myself in order to make sense out of life.

In Lesson 2 we learned that:
Whatever rules the heart will exercise inescapable influence over the life and behavior.

In Lesson 3 we learned that:
We have been united with Christ and indwelt by the Holy Spirit so that we can say "no" to the passions and desires of the sinful nature.

In Lesson 4 we learned that:

God has called us to be his ambassadors, faithfully representing his message, methods, and character ***(LOVE, KNOW, SPEAK, DO)***.

In Lesson 5 we learned that:

We must seek to build loving relationships in which the work of God can thrive.

In Lesson 6 we learned that:

God calls us to suffer so that we will be qualified agents of his comfort and compassion.

In Lesson 7 we learned that:

We need to ask questions that move us beyond the casual and help us to know when a person needs ministry.

In Lesson 8 we learned that:

We function as God's instruments of change by helping others think biblically about their situations and relationships, thoughts and motives, and behavior.

In Lesson 9 we learned that:

Confrontation must always be rooted in the comfort and call of the gospel.

In Lesson 10 we learned that:

To confront means to lead people to consider, confess, commit, and change.

In the last two lessons we will consider the final element of our personal ministry model, ***DO***. We will learn how to apply the insights we learn and the commitments we make to everyday life.

CONCEPTS AND OBJECTIVES

Concept: To help someone change, I must have a biblical agenda for change that reflects biblical commands, principles, promises, and priorities.

Personalized: I must always ask, "What are God's goals for change in me as I face relationships and situations?

Related to Others: In personal ministry, I must always ask, "How can I support this person in the process of change?"

LESSON CONTENT

Have you ever been encouraged by the promises of another person, only to have him fail to follow through? Have you ever had personal insights that did not lead to lasting change in your life? Have you ever made commitments that somehow got lost in the frenetic pace of life? Have you ever known that certain changes needed to take place, but you didn't know how to make them? Have you ever been confused as you tried to decide what things in your life were your responsibility and what things you could rightfully entrust to God? Have you ever benefited from someone holding you accountable? Have you ever felt that the changes that you need to make in your life are just impossible? These things will be our focus in the last two lessons. ***DO*** teaches us how to carefully apply the truths we have learned, the personal insights we have gained, and the commitments we have made to the situations and relationships of daily living.

To do this, the following four things are essential:

1. ***Establishing your personal ministry agenda.*** This gives you a sense of direction as you minister to another.

2. ***Clarifying responsibility.*** As people seek to apply truths to life, the issue of who is responsible for what will always come up.

3. ***Instilling identity in Christ.*** Since change is a hard process, it is important to remind people of the amazing resources that are theirs as children of God.

4. ***Providing accountability.*** Since change demands perseverance, we all need the encouragement, insight, and warning that a system of oversight will provide.

1. Establish Personal Ministry Agenda

It is hard to lead a person to change if you aren't sure where he should be going! Take time to establish your agenda. Does this sound too technical or formal for person-to-person ministry? Let's begin by defining our terms. An agenda is simply a plan for accomplishing a goal. It is nothing more than a map that shows us our destination (the changes that need to take place) and how to get there (the How? Where? When? With whom? that we must consider as we institute change). Since our goal is more than denouncing sin, and since we really do want to be God's instruments of lasting change, it is vital to know exactly where we are going and what we need to do to get there. This is where personal ministry becomes very practical, concrete, and specific: God is calling *this* person in *this* situation to *these* specific changes.

All too often, our personal ministry is at its weakest here. We will prepare for hours to teach a Sunday School class, but we will give someone very serious life advice on the spur of the moment, essentially out of our back pockets! Surely, the result is that much of our "ministry" to one another is not well thought out and therefore not solidly biblical. When we do not step back to establish a biblical sense of direction (agenda), our ministry is weakened by:

- Personal bias.
- Ignorance.
- Poor theology.
- Misunderstanding of Scripture.
- Improper application of Scripture.
- Fear of man.
- Emotional thinking.
- Pressure of the moment.

We should not speak to serious life issues impulsively and without preparation. We must step back and ask questions that will help us think clearly about God's goals for change for this person in this situation, and how to accomplish those goals. Let's consider three agenda-setting questions.

1. ***What does the Bible say about the information that has been gathered?*** We need to filter everything we have learned about this person through the grid of sound biblical thinking. (Refer to Figure 8-1 as a way to do this.) This protects our ministry from personal bias and unbiblical thinking. It enables us to speak as ambassadors, communicating clearly the message of the King.

2. ***What are God's goals for change for this person in this situation?*** Here we are applying God's call to put off and to put on **(Ephesians 4:22-24)** to the specifics of this person's thoughts, motives, and behavior. In this situation, with these people, what does God want him to think, desire, and do? In asking this question, we mark out our destination. We can't lead a person if we do not know where we are going, and in personal ministry we must only lead people where God is calling them to go.

3. ***What are biblical methods for accomplishing God's goals for change?*** This is the *how* of the change process. After clearly and specifically establishing biblical goals, we need to determine the best biblical means of accomplishing them. Often people will have a sense of what is wrong, but the way they seek to correct it complicates matters further. Let's say that you are ministering to a husband who confesses that he has not encouraged his wife as he should. It would not be biblical to advise him to bombard his wife with flattering words that are insincere. Nor would you advise a family in debt to have the husband work ninety hours a week! Biblical change is not only about the what, it must also include the *how*. To counsel wisely, you must know God's Word well, the situation well, and the person's heart motives well.

It is at this point that God will often surprise us. When our neighbor is mistreating us, it is not our first reaction to look for ways of doing good to him! When someone is angry with us, we don't tend to think that a soft answer will be part of the solution. The Bible not only lays out for us a surprising description of what is wrong with us, but also a surprising agenda for correction. How must this person put off what needs to be put off? How must this person put on what needs to be put on? For this person in this situation, what are the concrete steps of correction to which God is calling him?

2. Clarify Responsibility

One of the most important questions in life and therefore in personal ministry is: Who is responsible for what? As you function as one of God's instruments of change, you will encounter people who tend to be **irresponsible**. These people fail to shoulder the responsibilities to which God has clearly called them. You will also encounter those who are **overly responsible**. These people tend to take as their responsibility things that God has not called or enabled them to do.

The third class of people you will encounter is probably the biggest of the three. These are people who are **genuinely confused** when it comes to the issue of responsibility. They are not sure which things are their God-given job and which things they can entrust to him. Sometimes they are mini-messiahs, trying to do things that only God can do. Sometimes they ask God to do for them what he has clearly called them to do. All of the people mentioned here need a clear understanding of their responsibility as they seek to apply change to the specifics of daily life.

Figure 11-1 is a very simple tool for biblically clarifying responsibility. Let's work through the illustration together.

Let's start with the inner circle. This circle represents a particular person's biblical job description. These are the things that God, in his Word, calls this person to do in the midst of his present situation and relationships. He needs to have a clear sense of what God calls him to do as a husband, father, neighbor, relative, son, worker, and member of the body of Christ. Here we are calling the person to biblical discipleship, that is, to deny himself, take up his cross, and follow Christ **(Luke 9:23-25)**. Here we are calling him to no longer live for himself, but for the Lord **(2 Corinthians 5:14,15)**. Most importantly, we are making that call to discipleship clear and concrete.

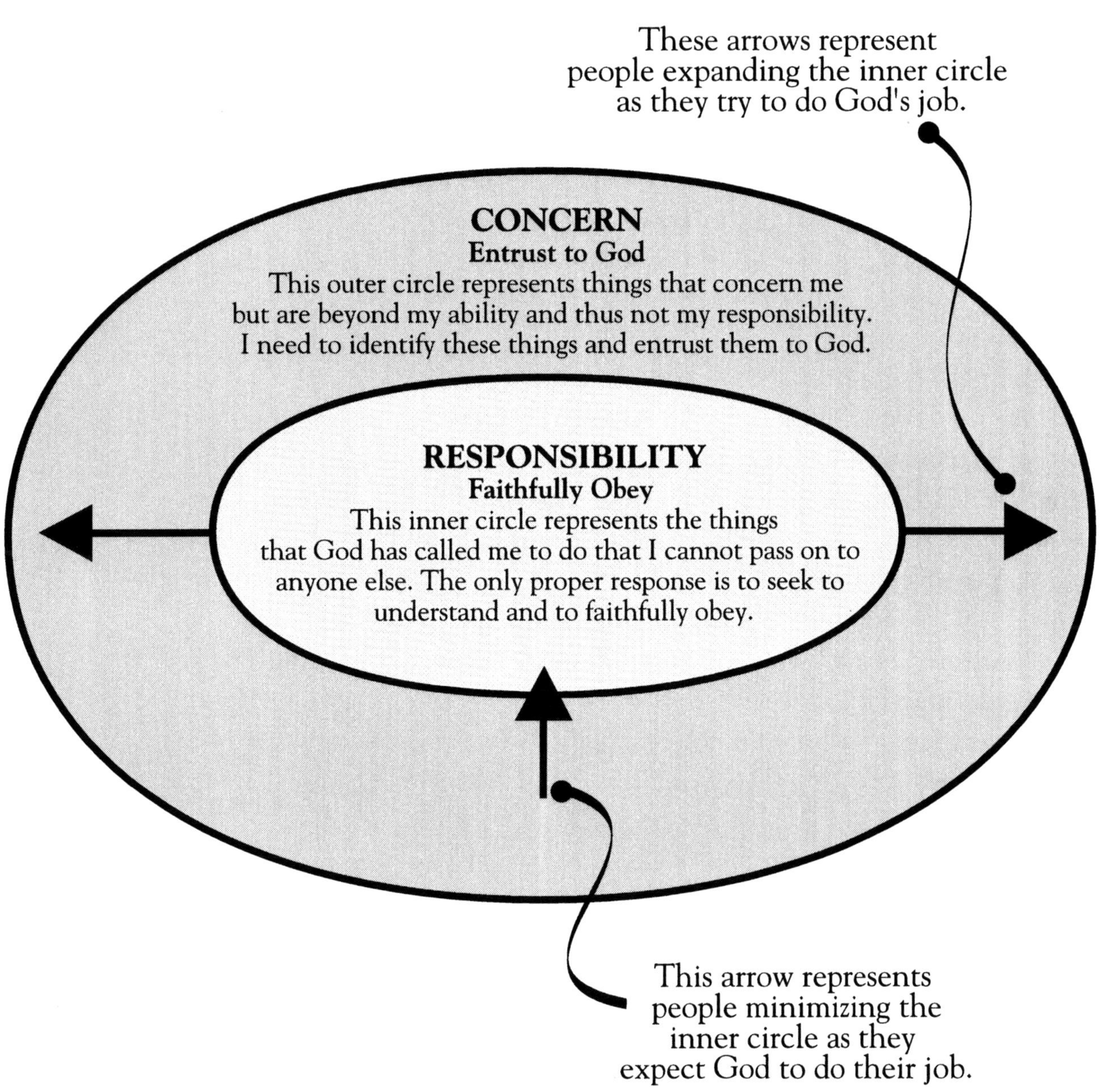

Figure 11-1. Clarifying Responsibility.

In this circle, we want the person to list what he thinks are his God-assigned duties in his relationships and situation. Then we want to examine his list in the light of Scripture, asking whether these things really are what God has called him to do.

The outer circle represents those things that are important to a person (the love of a spouse, a child's salvation, etc.), yet they are beyond her ability to bring about. Therefore, they are not her responsibility. Here we are calling a person to recognize her limits and to remember God, who is faithful to his promises **(Psalm 145:13)** and sovereign over all things **(Acts 17: 24-28)**.

It is very important to help the person see when she has allowed the inner circle to expand into the outer circle. In so doing, we are helping the person confess to where she has functioned as a mini-messiah, trying to do what only God can do. We also want to help the person to recognize and confess where she has tended to shrink the inner circle. In so doing, we are helping the person to identify places where she has, under the guise of trusting God, failed to do what God has called her to do.

Living as a mini-messiah (with too large an inner circle) has a two-sided negative effect. If I am trying to do God's job, I will experience discouragement, frustration, and failure. I will also tend to leave undone the job that God, in his Word, has clearly assigned to me.

For example, Alicia is concerned about her teenaged son, who is rebellious, irresponsible, unkind, and selfish. He is missing more school than he is attending. Alicia has told her friends that her goal is to "turn Matt into a responsible Christian human being if it is the last thing I ever do." This is the goal of a mini-messiah.

Attempting to give back to God what he has called me to do (too small an inner circle) will have a two-sided negative result as well. I will waste time and prayer if I wait for God to do something he has assigned me to do. He will empower me to do these things, but he will not do them for me. Therefore, I will be waiting for something I will not receive. And as I am waiting, things will worsen because of what I have left undone.

This is Sam's situation. He knows he has a broken relationship with Joe because of unkind things Sam said to him in public. Sam says he has "dealt with it in his heart" and is now waiting for God to restore the relationship. His inner circle is too small.

The Christian life is really a "trust and obey" lifestyle. I must always trust those things that are out of my control to God, and I must always be faithful to obey his clear and specific commands. **Romans 12:14-21** lays out this lifestyle for us in the context of mistreatment. God clearly explains our duty in the face of mistreatment:

- Bless those who persecute you (v.14).
- Commit to living in harmony (v.16).
- Do not be proud (v.16).
- As far as you can, live at peace with everyone (v.19).
- Meet your enemy's needs (v.20).
- Overcome evil with good (v.21).

Paul makes it clear that in moments of mistreatment, there are things that I must not take as my responsibility. Instead, I must entrust them to God. For example, I must not retaliate or seek revenge. These are things that by their very nature only God has the right and the power to do. They are things he has promised to do. I must not load them on my shoulders. So, God says, "Vengeance and repayment belong to me. You stay out of my way ('leave room for God's wrath') and let me handle it." So I must, in a spirit of joyful submission, do what God has called me to do, and in a spirit of humble trust, give to God what he alone can do.

There are few areas more confusing than the area of personal responsibility. People need practical clarity to help them through the process of change. It is a vital part of our ministry to the people we are called to help.

THE BIG QUESTION: Do you minister to others with a clear sense of biblical direction and help them clarify their responsibilities before God?

CPR

Concepts

1. The personal ministry process is not over at the point of insight. The insights that God has given a person must be applied to the situations and relationships of his or her daily life.

2. To help a person change, I must have a biblical sense of direction (agenda) that reflects God's commands, principles, promises, and priorities.

3. One of the most important ways of functioning as an instrument of change is to help a person clarify responsibility.

Personalized

1. I must determine whether I am applying the insights that God gives me to the specifics of my daily life.

2. I must ask myself, "Are there places where I am trying to do God's job and therefore failing to do what he has called me to do?"

3. In my own life, am I confusing personal insight with concrete biblical change?

Related to others

1. Am I looking for God-given opportunities to encourage others to entrust to God those things that are out of their control?

2. Am I helping people to arrive at a clear biblical job description for their relationships and life situations?

3. Do I take time to establish a sense of direction in personal ministry so I can guide people to where God wants them to be?

Helping Others Change
Make It Real

LESSON 11

As you continue to examine the ministry relationship(s) you have chosen to work on in your ***Personal Ministry Opportunity***, answer the following questions.

1. What portions of Scripture help you to understand this person (or group), his situation, and his struggle in response to it?

2. What are God's goals for change for this person (or this group)?

3. How might you be part of encouraging this change? Pray regularly about this.

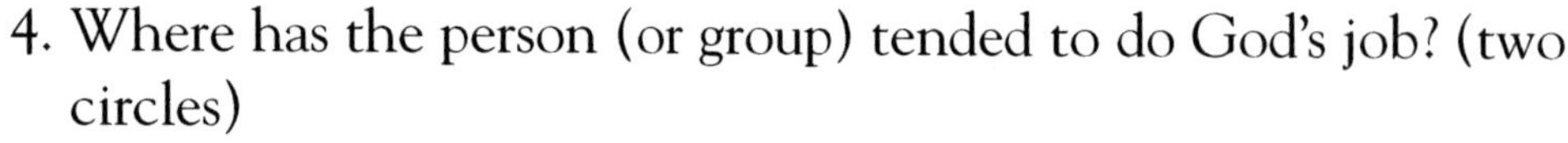

4. Where has the person (or group) tended to do God's job? (two circles)

5. Where has the person (or group) tended to wait for God to do what he has called him (or them) to do?

6. Have you clarified this issue of responsibility for him (or them)?

7. Where in your ministry to this person (or group) have you tended to be irresponsible, overly responsible, or confused?

DO II: Applying Change to Everyday Life

DISCUSS HOMEWORK

REVIEW

Truth #1: Above all, we need God and his truth to live as we were created to live **(Genesis 1:26ff; 2 Timothy 3:16,17)**. *Lesson 1*.

Truth #2: Each of us is called by God to be his instrument of change in the lives of others, beginning with our families and the body of Christ **(Ephesians 4:11-17; Colossians 3:15-17)**. *Lesson 1*.

Truth #3: Our behavior is rooted in the thoughts and motives of our hearts. People and situations only prompt our hearts to express themselves in words and actions **(Proverbs 4:23; Luke 6:43-45; Mark 7:21; Matthew 23:25; James 4:1-10)**. *Lessons 2-3*.

Truth #4: Christ has called us to be his ambassadors, following his message, methods, and character **(2 Corinthians 5:14-21)**. *Lesson 4*.

Truth #5: Being an instrument of change means incarnating the love of Christ by sharing in people's struggles, identifying with their suffering, and extending God's grace as we call them to change **(Colossians 3:12-14; Hebrews 2:10-11; Titus 2:11-3:8; 2 Corinthians 1:3-11)**. *Lessons 5-6.*

Truth #6: Being an instrument of change means seeking to know people by guarding against false assumptions, asking good questions, and interpreting in a way that is distinctly biblical **(Proverbs 20:5; Hebrews 4:14-16)**. *Lessons 7-8.*

Truth #7: Being an instrument of change means speaking the truth in love. With the gospel as comfort and call, I can help people to see themselves in God's Word and lead them to repentance **(Romans 8:1-17; Galatians 6:1-2; James 1:22-25)**. *Lessons 9-10.*

Truth #8: Being an instrument of change means helping people do what God calls them to do by clarifying responsibility, offering loving accountability, and reminding them of their identity in Christ **(Philippians 2:1-14; 2 Peter 1:3-9; 1 John 3:1-3; Galatians 6:2)**. *Lessons 11-12.*

CONCEPTS AND OBJECTIVES

Concept: Human beings always live out of some sense of identity. It is vital for the believer to understand his identity in Christ.

Personalized: I must always ask myself, "Do I view my life and myself from the vantage point of who I am in Christ?"

Related to others: Do I seek to provide encouragement and accountability to those who are following God's call to change?

LESSON CONTENT

Does it ever seem that the job God has assigned you is impossible? Are you ever overwhelmed by your responsibilities? Do you ever feel weak and unprepared? Do you encounter situations where you

lack practical wisdom? Have you ever found yourself failing at the same thing over and over again? Have you ever been discouraged at the height of God's standards? Have you ever thought it would be easier if you had someone standing with you? Have you ever felt as if you were left to struggle through change all alone? Have you ever thought that you would benefit from being accountable to someone else? Have you ever sought an accountability relationship, only to find that no one was willing or available?

This lesson teaches that encouragement and accountability are very important parts of the truth application process. We were never created to live in isolation. God has designed us to live in community, first with him and then with one another. In the hard process of change, we see our need for one another. We are not autonomous, self-sufficient beings. As I begin the process of change, I need your encouragement and oversight.

3. Instill Identity in Christ

Human beings are always living out of some kind of identity. We are sons, daughters, bosses, employees, parents, friends, neighbors, consumers, etc. Our sense of identity has a powerful influence on our choices and responses. As we call people to the hard process of change, it is important that they are living out of a gospel identity. They need to understand their position and resources as children of God.

It is easy to forget who we are as we deal with life in this fallen world, as we address age-old habits of thought, motive, and behavior, and apply new insights and commitments to daily living. This is why it is vital to keep reminding people of their identity in Christ. We want to stimulate the practical faith and courage that come from knowing who you are and what you have been given.

Peter addresses this issue in **2 Peter 1:3-9**. Let's consider the important points of this passage.

- Peter proposes (v.8) that there will be people who know the Lord, but whose lives are ineffective and unproductive. These

people do not produce the harvest of good fruit that you would expect from a believer.

- Peter says that these people do not produce the expected fruit of faith because they are missing essential character qualities (faith, goodness, knowledge, self-control, perseverance, godliness, brotherly kindness, and love). Because these qualities are not rooted in their hearts, they do not produce the expected fruit (vv. 5-8).

- When we see Christians who do not exhibit Christian character and are not producing good fruit, we ought to ask, "Why?" What is missing in these people? Peter says, "These people are missing character qualities that result in good fruit because they have forgotten who they are ("... nearsighted and blind, and has forgotten that he has been cleansed from his past sins," v.9). These people have lost sight of their identity in Christ, so they do not realize the position and resources that are theirs.

- Peter reminds us of one significant aspect of our identity—that in Christ we have been given "everything we need for life and godliness" (v.3). As the children of God, we are rich! We don't just have some things. We have all that we need!

Notice the tense of the verb in verse 3. Peter says that everything "has been given." The verb is in the perfect tense, which refers to an action in the past that has continuing results into the future. Peter is saying that the giving has already been done. It is not something we have to wait for. As a result of the redemptive work of Christ, everything we need has been placed in our storehouse. When he says "everything," what exactly does Peter mean? He tells us. We have everything that we need for "life and godliness." Peter is not only saying that God has provided all we need for eternal life, but for godliness as well. What does he mean by godliness? He means a God-honoring life from the time I am accepted into God's family until the time I go to be with him in eternity. We have been given everything we need to think, desire, and

behave in a godly way in the situations and relationships in which God has placed us! What an awesome provision!

- Peter tells us the purpose of this great provision. It is not so that we would be personally happy (nice job, marriage, family, church, neighborhood, vacations, retirement, etc.). No, God's purpose is that we would become participants in his divine nature! God's ultimate purpose is not personal happiness, but personal holiness. God is addressing my most significant need, which is not external or emotional, but moral. It is a heart ruled by the Lord rather than by "evil desires." If my heart is ruled by evil desires, I will participate in the "corruption in the world" rather than in the work of Christ. I will not have a harvest of good fruit. Peter is saying that the most significant thing that God saves us from is us! Because of his abundant supply, we no longer have to live "unto ourselves," but for "him who died for us and was raised again" **(2 Corinthians 5:15)**.

- Finally, Peter tells us what will happen when we start living out our identity in Christ (vv. 5-8). It will change the way we live. We will not settle for a little bit of Christian character. We will want all that God has provided. We will see the relationships and situations of daily life as opportunities to get in increasing measure what belongs to us in Christ. If you understand your identity, you will have a progressive growth paradigm for life. You will not look at life as a minefield. You will not live to avoid, escape, or defend. You will live with hope, expectancy, and courage. You will live as one who is rich, not poor.

As people begin to apply the new insights they have been given and the new commitments they have made, this is the identity they need. They will tend to forget who they are. (Moses: "Who I am, that I should go?" Gideon: "But Lord, how can I save Israel? My clan is the weakest...and I am the least in my family.") They need to be reminded of their position (children of God) and their resources (everything they need) over and over again.

4. Providing Accountability

As change is applied to daily living, the Bible gives us two things to remember. First, as we help restore a person to where God wants him to be, we should "carry each other's burdens" **(Galatians 6:2)**. We are also told that we should "encourage one another daily" **(Hebrews 3:13)**. These passages have much to offer us as we think about accountability.

Accountability is not about being a private detective.

It is not about trying to do the work of the Holy Spirit.

It is not about being someone's conscience.

It is not about forcing someone to obey.

It is not about chasing someone who is running or looking for someone who is hiding.

Accountability is about providing loving structure, guidance, assistance, encouragement, and warning to a person who is fully committed to the change God is working in his life. Let's look at these elements of accountability.

1. ***Accountability provides structure.*** Life is often messy and chaotic. Change seems easier when being discussed than it does when being applied to life. Accountability provides an outside system of structure ("Do these things during this period of time") that can be immensely helpful to the person attempting something for the first time.

2. ***Accountability provides guidance.*** Often a person will want to do what is right but won't be sure how to do it. At these times it is a great benefit to have someone standing alongside to provide ongoing wisdom as to the "where," "when," and "how" of change.

3. ***Accountability provides assistance.*** There are times when the person is not able to make the needed changes alone (example: a difficult talk with a wife, friend, child) and he literally needs someone there with him, helping him make the changes that are needed.

4. ***Accountability provides encouragement.*** Change is hard and people get beaten down. They are tempted to question their commitments or even to quit. In these times, they need someone they trust alongside them, who knows their situation and who can encourage them to continue.

5. ***Accountability provides warning.*** There are times when people confess the need for change, but then begin to rebel against it when they realize the cost and work involved. These people need to be warned of the consequences that their disobedience and rebellion will bring. They need to be reminded that they will harvest what they have sown **(Galatians 6:7)**.

Accountability is not about chasing a person who does not want to change, or trying to do the work of the Holy Spirit. It is the willingness to provide ongoing help to the person who is fully committed to the "put off – put on" process.

There are three questions to ask as you seek to provide ongoing accountability.

> What kinds of ongoing help will this person need?
>
> How often will I need to be in contact with him for change to continue?
>
> Are there other resources in the Body of Christ that would be helpful during this period of change? How can I connect this person to those resources?

Remember, as the person begins to apply new insights and new commitments to his situations and relationships, it is important to remind him of his identity in Christ and to provide ongoing accountability.

THE BIG QUESTION: Do you help others bear the burden of change by providing biblical accountability and affirming their identity in Christ?

CPR

Concepts

1. Human beings always live out of some sense of identity.

2. Every believer needs to understand his union with Christ.

3. In times of change, each of us needs loving accountability.

Personalized

1. Do I look at myself and my life from the perspective of who I am in Christ?

2. Does a daily recognition of my identity in Christ shape the way I think, speak, and act?

3. Do I humbly seek and receive accountability as God calls me to change?

Related to others

1. Do I look for opportunities to remind others of their identity in Christ?

2. Do I look for where and how I can help others bear the load of change?

3. Am I willing to provide loving accountability to others as they apply new insights and commitments to their daily lives?

Helping Others Change
Make It Real

LESSON 12

Consider your ***Personal Ministry Opportunity*** using the following questions.

1. What kind of accountability do you need to supply so that change and growth will continue to take place?

2. Where has this person (group) tended to forget who he is in Christ? What Scripture passages could you use to encourage a clear sense of this identity?

3. Describe how you would use one of these passages with the person.

4. Look back over your work on your ***Personal Ministry Opportunity*** and list some of the specific things you have learned about being an instrument of change in God's redemptive hands.

5. What prayer requests do you have for the person you have sought to serve? What prayer requests do you have for yourself?

Helping Others Change
At A Glance

3. Understanding your heart struggle.
James 4:1-10

4. Following the Wonderful Counselor in personal ministry.
2 Corinthians 5:14-20

2.

What rules the heart will shape and direct the behavior.
Ezekiel 14:1-5

5. 6.

Love: *John 13:34*

Building relationships in which God's work will thrive.

7. 8.

Know: *Hebrews 4:14-16*

Getting to know people, discovering where change is needed.

9. 10.

Speak: *Proverbs 20:5*

Speaking the truth in love.

11. 12.

Do: *Galatians 6:1,2*

Applying change to everyday life.

1. Three Questions Everyone Asks:

1. Why do people do the things they do?
2. How does lasting change take place?
3. How can I be an instrument of change in the life of another?

FIRM FOUNDATION

Creation—Fall—Redemption

Genesis 1, Genesis 3, Hebrews 3:12,13

Each one needing help, each one called to be a helper.

Notes

introducing the exclusive

Black *Dining Card*

Use your Black Dining Card as many times as you like and ***you*** choose which offer you would like - **either** £5 off, 10% off **or** a Bottle of House Wine. Subject to the RULES OF USE below.

RESTRICTED issue (250 only) available to THE FOODIE GUIDE readers

To apply for your Black Dining Card please fill in the form below and send together with your payment to:
FREEPOST RSKB-RHRA-RZBT, The Foodie Square Guide Ltd, 373 Welford Rd, Northampton, NN2 8PT

Cardholder Name ....
Address ....
....
....
Postcode ....
Email ....
Tel. ....

To receive your exclusive Black Dining Card please enclose a cheque payable to The Foodie Square Guide Ltd for £5. Only one card per cardholder will be issued. Every card has a unique number and can only be issued once. No replacements will be supplied. PLEASE READ THE RULES OF USE.

CARDHOLDER RULES OF USE

1. THE FOODIE GUIDE Black Dining Card may not be used in conjunction with any other offers, including FOODIE Vouchers.
2. The card entitles the cardholder to choose **either** £5 off, 10% off **or** a Bottle of House Wine when spending £30 or more on any day of the week and at any time, except on the following: **NOT ACCEPTED during December, Mothers Day, Fathers Day or Valentines Day.**
3. Only one card up to a maximum of 6 covers per table/party may be used with a minimum total spend of £30.
4. The card is only accepted at participating restaurants displaying The Black Dining Card symbol within THE FOODIE GUIDE Edition 8. **DC**
5. This card has no cash value and is valid until 30/09/2011.
6. Cardholders must mention THE FOODIE GUIDE Black Dining Card when making a telephone booking. Failure to do so may result in the offer being refused.

Join the growing FOODIE family and check out our website at

www.thefoodieguide.co.uk

Become a "Taste Buddy" and recommend / review restaurants. Watch video clips of chefs at work or check out the latest news from your favourite restaurants, delis and farm shops.

Contents

To find an establishment, look for it's entry number on each page

THE FOODIE voucher symbols: **Please check individual entries for which FOODIE vouchers are accepted and any establishment terms (terms and conditions apply)**

Introduction

Welcome to our 8th edition of THE FOODIE GUIDE. You will notice that we have made a few changes, mainly to keep pace with our website. We now have a supplementary list of restaurants, which have been recommended to us by our readers over the past 12 months. As your comments to us prove, these restaurants each have much to offer and you certainly think they are worthy of an entry in our guide. Keep those recommendations coming in and we will hopefully be able to include even more next time.

We have also introduced for the first time (and with very limited availability) our Black Dining Card. This card is exclusive to us and only 250 are being made available. The card will be more convenient for those who love using our Foodie Vouchers but sometimes forget to take them to the restaurant. Keep it close at hand and you can choose to claim either £5 off or 10% off your meal or a free bottle of house wine when you visit a participating restaurant. Just look at the entries in the guide and you will see which restaurants are accepting them. We expect to add more restaurants to this programme over the coming months and will show these on our website, so keep visiting us.

We have been delighted to see that the Farm Shops and Delis are going from strength to strength. We have included even more in this edition and hope you enjoy visiting them as much as we have.

Lastly, I would just like to say that although it is said "imitation is the sincerest form of flattery", we do not wish to be confused with any other food guides available in the four counties. All the restaurants featured in our guide have been recommended to us by our readers, therefore, THE FOODIE GUIDE is unique. I would like to say a big thank you to all the readers who have contacted us and I look forward to the coming 12 months in anticipation of finding more incredible places to eat out.

Paul Allen
Editor

photograph courtesy of Mash & Co.

Foreword

by our guest chef for this year
Olivier Bertho

I am so lucky to live and work in such a beautiful part of the country, where we have a wealth of fabulous restaurants, great local food suppliers and of course organisations like The Foodie Guide, who continue to be at the forefront of promoting great food in the region.

For me though, it is simply all about cooking. It's what makes me tick! I've been doing it for over 25 years and I am still as passionate about food as when I started out all those years ago. Being able to pass on my knowledge and support young chefs coming into the industry continues to be another rewarding factor in my career and gives me great satisfaction.

However, it is ultimately our restaurant guests that make it all worthwhile. A great restaurant is not just about the food but the complete guest experience. I am really proud to work with such a dedicated team and we all look forward to welcoming more Foodie Guide members over the coming year.

Olivier Bertho
Head Chef
Oliviers Restaurant, Woburn.

Food for thought

In December 2006 when we took over The Navigation Inn, the food offer was typically pre-cooked generic pub food served by people who at that time had little passion for food or what they were producing/removing from a packet. Coming from a 100 percent freshly produced food environment I was alarmed at what I saw. Worst of all I now owned the business!

For the business to even stand still in the changing market which was seeing more demanding, knowledgeable, food conscious customers, things had to change. For me as a Chef things couldn't change quickly enough.

Inspite of what I felt about the existing menu a number of regulars at the time amazingly seemed to like the current offer. Radical change wasn't going to be possible. So slowly I integrated freshly made dishes of similar style at the same prices to maintain the current turnover. The hardest thing for me was that this often was not appreciated by some who tried to demand the old menu items back. Going back was never an option and we lost numerous customers who had frequented the place for a number of years.

Whilst focusing on the new menu, trying to inspire chefs who had very little interest, I was trying to renovate a very old tired looking venue. The joys of working for yourself. I realised I was no longer a chef but a restaurateur and a chef. This combination makes for a very hectic life. Especially when your premises are over 200 years old and in constant need of work.

To move forward we needed to attract new customers. It was a few months before there was any noticeable change. Compliments were received for our new menu and the word slowly started to get out. It was great to finally hear customers agreeing about the merits of fresh food.

Almost four years on and The Navigation Inn is a different venue, so far away from The Navigation Inn we had bought. Now a very successful destination food establishment, which people are prepared to travel to for our exciting freshly cooked menu.

Opened in January, Cameron's our fine dining restaurant is the next step in the impressive development of The Navigation Inn.

Fresh food and drink with traceability and building relationships with local suppliers is the future of the hospitality industry. A future in which customers are becoming more and more educated and have higher expectations.

I believe it is the responsibility of everyone of us; restaurateurs, customers, suppliers, chefs and growers to keep raising the bar and turn the United Kingdom into a forward thinking nation which can finally be proud of its food industry.

Dan Cameron
Chef/Owner
The Navigation Inn, Cosgrove

nglish Asparagus Toast,
Oven Dried Parm Ham,
Beefste mato & M
Basil Muffin Chopped S
£7.0

61 High Street
Woburn Sands
Buckinghamshire
MK17 8QY
Tel: 01908 584385
Email: mail@thepurplegoose.co.uk
www.thepurplegoose.co.uk

THE PURPLE GOOSE RESTAURANT

High quality classic cuisine with a modern twist

The Purple Goose Restaurant - passionate about great food and wine, has a simple philosophy; Interesting starters, locally sourced produce, high quality meats and fish, enticing vegetarian options, delicious homemade desserts and an extensive cheeseboard. Add to this an interesting and well thought out wine list with friendly service and you have a dining experience to remember. Head Chef and joint proprietor Scott Ludlow is keen to impress and happy to accommodate dietary requirements be it Coeliac, Veggie or Dairy-free.

"We prepare and serve classic British cuisine with a continental influence and modern twist as well as top quality steaks cooked on our chargrill. Maybe you will try our 4 hour slow cooked belly pork or fresh fish delivered from the fish market in Devon."

The Purple Goose offers relaxed but focused service. That waitress who doesn't know what the 'Soup Of The Day' is? The one who forgets to mention the 'Daily Specials'? Well she doesn't work at The Purple Goose!

The Purple Room is a quiet and intimate, completely private dining room where you can have a special dinner or perhaps a private business lunch. The Purple Room can seat up to 6 guests with private lounge area for coffee or drinks. Included in The Purple Room rates are: Glass of Champagne (or your choice of drink), Chef's Canapés, Bottled Still and Sparkling Water, Fresh Flowers, No Rush Policy - The Purple Room is yours for the whole lunch or dinner service.

FOODIE
Reader Comment

"This is fine dining at affordable prices in a small intimate setting. I will be going back." M.O.

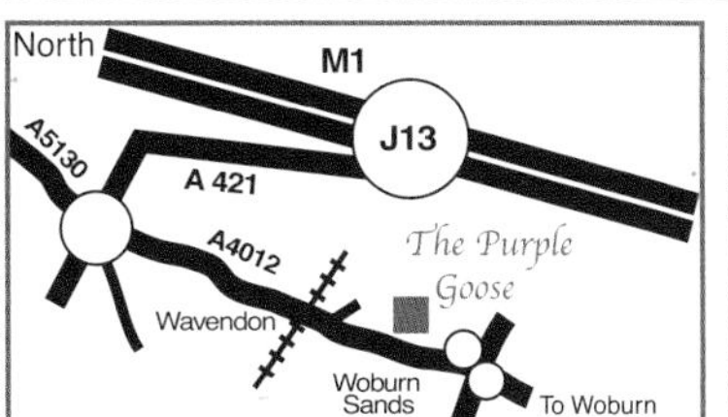

Vouchers valid Tuesday to Friday only

10%

Food service times:
Tue 6.30 pm - 9.30pm
Wed - Sat 12.00 pm - 2.00 pm & 6.30 pm - 9.30pm
Sun 12.00 pm - 2.30 pm

The Betsey Wynne

21 Mursley Road
Swanbourne
Buckinghamshire
MK17 0SH
Tel: 01296 720825
Email: info@thebetseywynne.co.uk
www.thebetseywynne.co.uk

FOODIE
Reader Comment

"Staff are friendly, service is excellent and the food is fantastic, simple but extremely well cooked and presented."

R.M.

The Betsey Wynne is part of the Swanbourne Estate in the small village of Swanbourne in North Buckinghamshire which has been owned by the Fremantle family for over 200 years. The opening of The Betsey Wynne, named after one of the Estate's colourful ancestors, is the result of many years of careful planning by the Estate and a quiet determination by the present owner to preserve and promote country life.

Built by the Swanbourne Estate in true local style, this free house has a large bar, comfortable leather sofas, open log fires and an impressive oak beamed dining hall. The snug, with its large inglenook fireplace and flagstone floor is suitable for meetings or private dining. In the summer, guests can enjoy the large garden with an old red tractor and play house for children and a terrace area for alfresco dining overlooking the open countryside.

Kevin Close is the Chef/Landlord, a popular Northern chef with an eye for detail, who favours classic English cuisine. A former landlord and restaurant owner with years of experience, including chef at the "Mild May" at the Glyndebourne Opera, now part of The Betsey Wynne folklore.

The Betsey Wynne aims to be a true "local" farm pub. Using their farm's own produce and supporting other local farmers as far as possible. The beef comes from the Home Farm's herd of pedigree Aberdeen Angus cows. The lamb on the menu comes from the flock of pedigree Hampshire Down sheep, which some butchers refer to as the "Aberdeen Angus equivalent of the lamb counter". They have exceptional eating quality - juicy, tender and a wonderful flavour. The pork comes from a variety of local producers. Sausages are made by Betsy Duncan Smith, who also cures her hams for the pub from her Saddleback and Large Black pigs. Both are traditional native breeds, full of flavour and reared traditionally in Swanbourne. Poultry is sourced from various local suppliers depending on produce required for menus. Seasonal game and venison is sourced where possible from nearby estates and primarily the Claydon Estate. From time to time 'specials' include pheasant, partridge, pigeon and rabbit.

The Estate has reinstated a traditional orchard to produce apples, pears, plums, mulberries, quince and figs. The Fremantle family's walled garden has also been revived and under Philip Dalton, the head gardener, now produces herbs and a variety of vegetables and soft fruit.

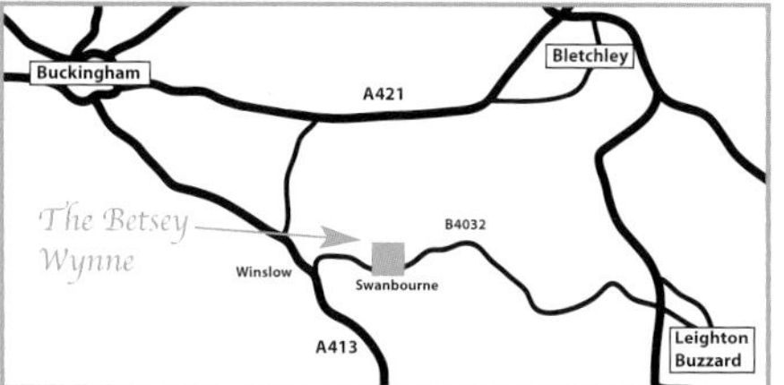

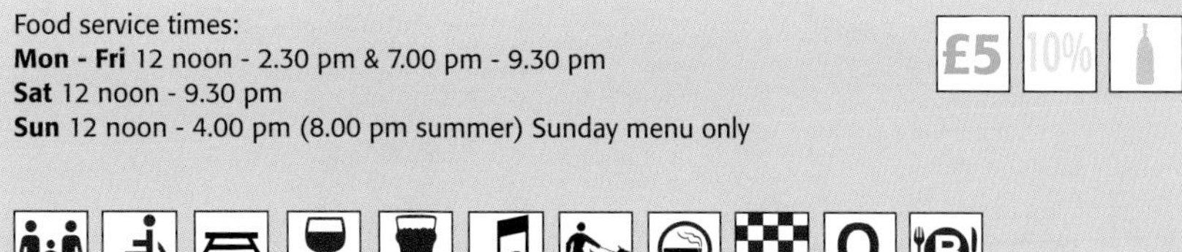

A contemporary award winning restaurant in a traditional country pub

The Crooked Billet

2 Westbrook End
Newton Longville
Bucks
MK17 0DF
Tel: 01908 373936
Fax: 01908 631979
www.thebillet.co.uk

"Still my favourite and still hard to beat, they serve some great food."
S.K.

"THE FOODIE Award 2004, 2006, 2007 & 2010 - Bucks" - THE FOODIE GUIDE
"50 best restaurants in the UK" - The Independent Guide
"Gastro Pub Of The Year" - The Times
"Wine Pub Of The Year" - The Good Pub Guide
"Inspectors Favourite Restaurant" - Michelin Guide to Pubs
"One of the best restaurants outside of London" - Tatler Guide

All our food comes from suppliers as local as possible. We could not do what we do without thanks to the following people:

The people of Newton Longville for growing our vegetables and herbs; Padbury Meat; Windmill Farm Pork; George Foster Goats Cheese; Old Smokies Smokehouse Newton Longville; Melchy's Smokehouse Newton Longville; Mr Barry Pugh for Suckling Pig; Ashridge Estate Game; Harvey's and Sons for Crab; Chinn Family at Cobrey Farm Asparagus; Higher Heath Farm Chicken; The Shooters at Thrift Wood for some of our Game Birds; Round Green Farm Venison; White House Farm Free Range Eggs; Mrs Tilley for Lamb and Mutton; Andy and Derrick, Brixham Day Boats; Chef's Connection, Covent Garden; Captain Tom for the Herbs and Chutney; Island Divers for the Shellfish, Isle of Man; Celtic Seafare Divers for our Scallops; Taylor's Mustards; the many Cheese Makers in the UK; Keen's Dairy for the Whey Butter, Wincanton; Eileen the Cleaner; Anthony Byrne Fine Wines; Woods Farm Beef; June for the Flowers and Dr Illy of Illy Caffe.

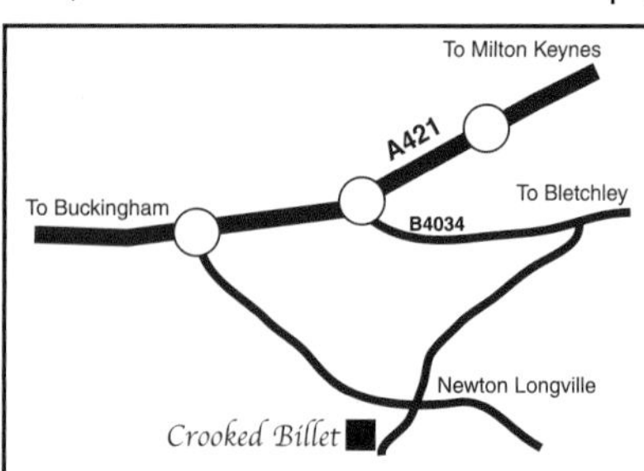

Lemon Cheesecake, Lemon Curd Ice Cream, Lemon Jelly

Sticky Toffee Gingerbread, Roasted Plums, Yellow Plum Ice Cream

Food service times:
Lunch - **Tues-Sat** 12 noon - 2.00 pm **Sun** 12.30 pm - 4.00 pm
Dinner - **Mon-Thurs** 7.00 pm - 9.30 pm **Fri-Sat** 6.30 pm - 10.00 pm

Vouchers not valid Fri or Sat evening

Roast Local Beef Fillet, Fondant Potato, Spring Vegetable Fricassee

Sea Bass Fillet, Crispy Shallot, Crushed Garden Potatoes, Roasted Greenhouse Tomatoes

Lobster, Local Asparagus, Poached Free Range Hens Egg

Different Flavoured Homemade Bread, Every Day

Roasted Scallop, Linquini, Champagne Butter Sauce, Caviar

Slowly Roasted Old Spot Pork Belly, Calvados Roasted Apple

THE CARRINGTON ARMS

Cranfield Road
Moulsoe
Newport Pagnell
MK16 0HB
Tel: 01908 218050
Fax: 01908 217850
Email: enquiries@thecarringtonarms.co.uk
www.thecarringtonarms.co.uk

FOODIE
Reader Comment

"The ability to select your own fresh, raw meat or fish from this restaurant makes this quite a special and unique place." L.C.

The Carrington Arms is an imposing 19th century listed building only one mile from junction 14 of the M1 in the picturesque village of Moulsoe.

This award winning pub/restaurant probably has the largest selection of meats and seafood on offer in the area. All are imaginatively displayed in a large chilled counter for you to choose, the selection includes some of the best local meats including their Prime 21 Day Dry Aged Bedfordshire Beef and Live Native Lobster tank in the restaurant. Everything is priced by weight. A good recommendation is The Carrington Arms famous "Bourbon Steak". Your selection is then grilled in front of you in the open kitchen to your liking. Also choose from their A La Carte Menu with freshly prepared seasonal British Dishes including Scallops and Black Pudding, Wood Pigeon, Oakley Lamb Rack and The Carrington Arms' Mixed Grill. There is also a lunchtime menu for those with less time with favourites like, Beer Battered Fish and Chips and Woburn Black Ham, Egg and Chips.

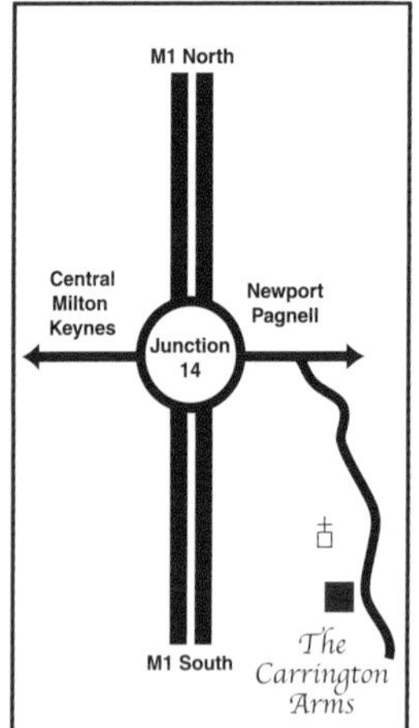

There are eight recently refurbished ensuite chalet style bedrooms within the gardens, each with a flat screen television, tea and coffee facilities and continental breakfast.

You can also just drop in for a drink, with an extensive wine list and a great selection of Real Ales (Some from local Breweries). It is recommended to book your table if you intend to have a meal to avoid disappointment. There is ample parking to the side of the restaurant.

Food service times:
Mon-Fri 12 noon - 2.30 pm &
6.00 pm - 10.00 pm
Sat 12 noon - 10.00 pm
Sun 12 noon - 9.30 pm

The Carriage House Restaurant

Claydon House
Middle Claydon
Buckinghamshire
MK18 2EX
Tel: 01296 730004
Email: eat@thecarriagehouserestaurant.co.uk
www.thecarriagehouserestaurant.co.uk

Within the courtyard of the magnificent Claydon House Estate, you'll find The Carriage House Restaurant, offering you renowned cuisine surrounded by beautiful gardens and breathtaking parkland.

Following 18 exciting years running Oxfordshire's famous restaurant boat, "Rosamund The Fair", the owners, Tim Matthews and Sophia Goodford, have now transformed The Carriage House Restaurant into an opulent dining room experience that's hard to resist.

Head Chef/Proprietor Tim Matthews and his team use only the very best, carefully sourced produce, offering you beautiful modern British cuisine. The finest meats from local butchers, fresh game from the estate and seasonal fruit and vegetables from the kitchen garden are all used to create delicious and imaginative dishes for you to savour.

The menus change regularly with the restaurant open for fine dining on the 1st Saturday of every month, for special events on the 3rd Saturday of every month and for light lunches every day except Thursdays. Why not look at our current special events listed on our website, along with our lunchtime menu? On Sundays, you'll find indulgent two and three course lunches. Plus, if you're in the mood for something a little lighter, a mouth-watering lunch menu is served throughout the year.

The ideal venue for weddings, parties and corporate events, you can enjoy exclusive use of the restaurant any day of the week. A quiet, professional approach ensures your event is truly memorable.

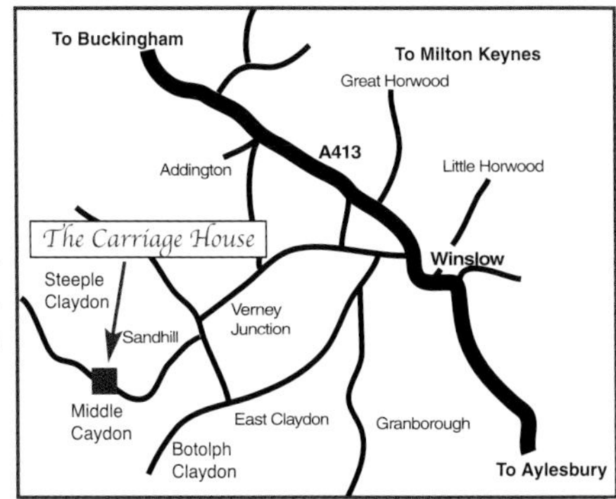

FOODIE
Reader Comment

"This is a must visit restaurant, lovely food in a nice setting. If you go for lunch you can take a walk around the gardens"

J.W.

Food service times:
Mon-Wed 12 noon - 3.00 pm
Thur Closed
Fri-Sun 12 noon - 3.00 pm
Fine Dining and Special Events from 7.00pm (bookings required)

£5

Lunch Dinner

Castlethorpe Road, Cosgrove, Milton Keynes MK19 7BE
Tel: 01908 543156
Email: info@navigationinn.net
www.navigationinn.net

FOODIE
Reader Comment

"We often wonder what the 'secret ingredient' is in some dishes. Absolutely delicious."
T.B.

The Navigation Inn is a family run pub restaurant that sits alongside the Grand Union Canal between Cosgrove and Castlethorpe, just a ten minute drive from Central Milton Keynes. Recently voted in the top ten waterside pubs in the UK in a Sunday Telegraph poll, a visit here will not disappoint, whether it's a quick pint or a three course meal that you're after.

Since the Cameron's took over in 2007, The Navigation Inn has quickly gained a reputation for serving excellent quality food. All the food at The Navigation Inn is freshly prepared in their kitchen using locally sourced produce wherever possible. The Navigation Inn also supports the Wolverton based charity Growing People who supply organically grown fruit and vegetables. It's not just the food that's fantastic at The Navigation Inn, all the staff will do everything possible to ensure you enjoy your time there.

All in all, The Navigation Inn is a fantastic place to go if you want an amazing meal, good service and one of the best views in the area. We thoroughly recommend booking to avoid any disappointment.

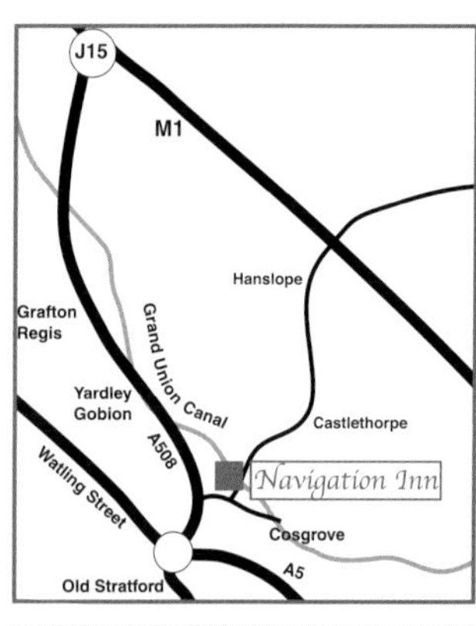

Food service times:
Mon-Thur 12 noon - 2.30 pm & 6.00 pm - 9.00 pm
Fri-Sat 12 noon - 2.30 pm & 6.00 pm - 9.30 pm
Sun 12 noon - 5.00 pm
Summer: Fri-Sun 12 noon - 9.30 pm

DC

Castlethorpe Road, Cosgrove, Milton Keynes MK19 7BE
Tel: 01908 543156
Email: info@navigationinn.net
www.navigationinn.net

Opened in January 2010, Cameron's, is the first independent restaurant venture of Dan Cameron, previously of Gordon Ramsay's Maze and ex-student of Leith's School of Food and Wine. Having his talent recognised by judges on BBC Masterchef Professionals back in 2008 earning himself a place in the final, Dan is delighted to be offering something unique in an area not known for destination restaurants.

Keen that the dining experience in his restaurant should surpass that of London restaurants, Cameron's has quickly gained a strong reputation locally, with experienced diners comparing it favourably with highly regarded and well-known establishments.

- Cameron's offers a relaxed environment with canal views.
- Extensive wine list. Fine wines dating back to 1966.
- Locally sourced, seasonal menu.
- A tasting menu with wine flights.

FOODIE
Reader Comment

"Cameron's is exquisite! They have raised the bar for fine dining in Bucks"

A.L.

Food service times:
Sat 6.00 pm - 9.00 pm

DC

THE BULL INN

OLNEY

9 Market Place
Olney
Buckinghamshire MK46 4EA
Tel: 01234 711470
Fax: 01234 241862
Email: thebullolney@gmail.com
www.thebullolney.com

Situated in the heart of Olney's market place is the 400 year old Bull Inn, formerly a coaching inn for the landed gentry. The Bulls character, warmth, friendly and professional service makes it a perfect venue for any occasion.

The Bull has a well earned reputation for well kept cask ales and is renowned for Sunday lunches in addition to a freshly prepared, varied menu which attracts visitors from all over the local area. Extensive gardens and walled courtyards make the Bull an ideal place to unwind and relax.

James Lomax and Mark Girling (pictured right), both chefs with over 30 years experience between them, aim to provide simple well cooked food, made from the best ingredients and sourced locally whenever possible.

The menu changes regularly to reflect the changing seasons and availability of fresh local produce.

The Bull's Function Suite caters for up to 80 people, and has its own access, bar and toilets. The room can be used for Training, Presentations, Conferences, Dinners or Parties.

To Wellingborough
A509
Olney High St
The Bull Inn
Co-op
Market Square
To Weston Underwood
To Milton Keynes

Food service times:
Mon-Fri 12 noon - 2.30 pm & 6.00 pm - 9.30 pm
Sat 12 noon - 4.00 pm & 6.00 pm - 9.30 pm
Sun 12 noon - 4.00 pm

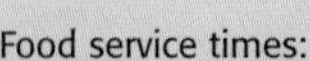

FOODIE
Reader Comment

"Had a great lunch out in the garden area, food/service was really good and kids were happy too!" G.S.

London Road
Little Kingshill
Great Missenden
Bucks HP16 0DG
Tel: 01494 862200
Fax: 01494 862945
Email: goodfood@nagsheadbucks.com
www.nagsheadbucks.co.uk

THE NAGS HEAD
15TH CENTURY
COUNTRY INN & RESTAURANT

AA Rosette for Culinary Excellence
AA 4 Star Inn
AA Pick of the Pubs
"Newcomer of the Year 2009" – The Publican Regional Award

The Nags Head in Great Missenden, Buckinghamshire is a traditional 15th century country Inn and restaurant situated along the valley of the River Misbourne in the glorious Chiltern Hills.

Brought to you by the Michaels family, owners of the award-winning Bricklayers Arms in Flaunden, Hertfordshire, the newly refurbished Nags Head serves an Anglo French fusion menu. The Nags Head has now been awarded with its first "Rosette" for its "Culinary Excellence" and accredited in several guides including a Commendation Award in the Hardens Guide; chosen as "Pick of the Pubs" in the AA Pub Guide and a recommendation and on the front cover of the Michelins "Eating Out in Pubs" and the much coveted "Michelin Guide".

The Nags Head was recently featured in the movie, Mr Fantastic Fox as it was an old favourite of children's author, Roald Dahl.

Dining guests will receive a warm welcome by Adam Michaels and his team who has recently been awarded one of the "Newcomer of the Year 2009" Awards by the Publican Magazine. The newly refurbished Nags Head keeps all of its original features, including a large inglenook fireplace and low old oak beams, and many new features including a new bar and stylish new furnishings throughout.

Now graded as an AA 4 star Inn, there are half a dozen new double and twin bedrooms, all beautifully refurbished with bath or shower ensuites After a rested night's sleep, you'll find a hearty breakfast waiting for you in the morning

Food is our passion; we use only the finest produce when available because we know it makes a difference and wherever possible, we source from local farms and suppliers. We believe in giving good value for money and serve only the finest quality food, so you can be assured of an excellent meal, time and time again. On the lunch and evening menus, you'll find favourites, such as home smoked fishes; mixed and wild mushroom feuillette; our famous 21 day aged Bedfordshire Fillet Steaks with a selection of sauces along with a great steak and kidney ale pie and local game. Fresh fish dishes are sourced according to market availability and change on a daily basis.

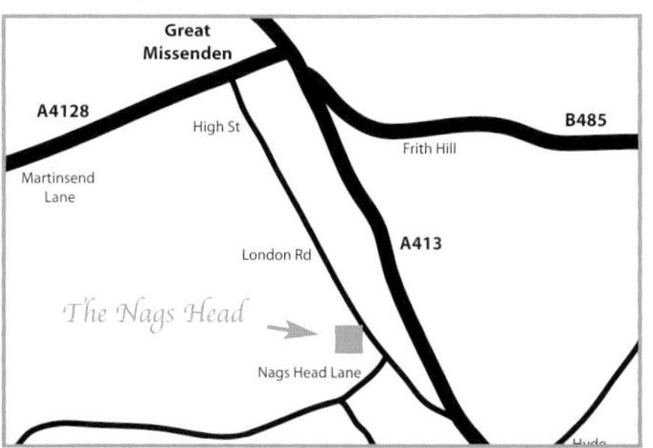

Don't miss out on our Sunday roasts where you'll find locally supplied fresh produce and mouthwatering puddings, along with an extensive award winning wine list to suit all tastes, as well as a selection of local ales.

Our bar is a great place to relax in front of the open fire place and in the summer months you can enjoy a drink or meal in our delightful garden with attractive views of rolling hills of the Chilterns.

Food service times:
Mon-Sat 12 noon - 2.30 pm & 6.30 - 9.30 pm
Sun 12 noon - 3.30 pm & 6.30pm - 8.30 pm

£5

FOODIE
Reader Comment

"The food never fails to delight and is thoughtfully prepared. A must visit for any foodie" T.B.

THE PLOUGH *at Simpson*

Simpson Road, Simpson Village, Milton Keynes MK6 3AH
Tel: 01908 691555
Fax: 01908 696915
Email: theploughatsimpson@hotmail.com
www.theploughatsimpson.co.uk

FOODIE
Reader Comment

"The quality of the food is way above what you would expect from this canalside pub - a hidden gem!"
G.L.

Set in the old village of Simpson on the banks of the Grand union Canal and only 5 minutes from Central Milton Keynes, The Plough provides a friendly personal welcome away from the chain establishments and the hustle and bustle of the city.

Now well established and known for a great selection of fine wines, real ales and freshly prepared food The Plough continues to pick up local awards and was named CAMRA PUB OF THE SEASON 2010 for the Milton Keynes and north Bucks area. They are also found in the Good Beer Guide 2010.

With both traditional bar fare, à la carte dining, and when the weather permits canal side BBQ's you can find something on the menu to suite your tastes and budget. Being independently owned the Plough also has a reputation for offering excellent bespoke celebration menus and that personal service for events such as wedding lunches, christenings, funeral buffets and birthday parties.

For lunch time dinners with limited time the Plough also offers a very popular "pre-order" arrangement. Safe in the knowledge that you will have a table reserved for you when you arrive and your meals be ready within minutes. It means you can enjoy lunch at a slower pace or even fit in time for dessert and coffee before you need to return to work.

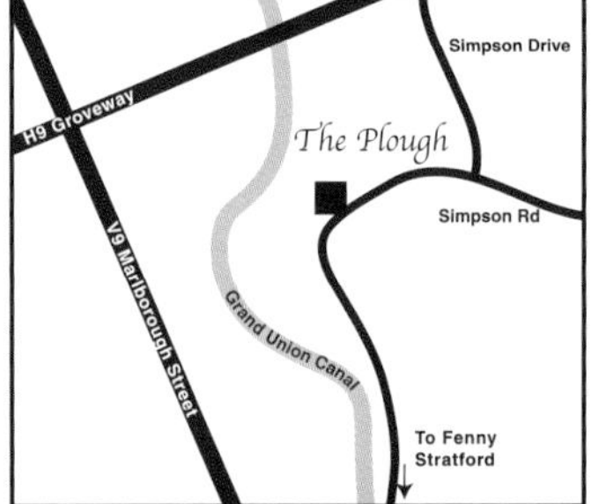

Highly recommended on many local websites and blogs come and see for yourself this hidden gem. Once you have visited you will be welcomed back again and again.

Food service times:
Mon-Thur 12 noon - 2.15 pm & 6.00 pm - 9.30 pm
Fri 12 noon - 2.15 pm & 6.00 pm - 10.00 pm
Sat 12 noon - 10.00 pm
Sun 12 noon - 4.00 pm

Rajdhani

706 Midsummer Boulevard
Food Centre
Central Milton Keynes
MK9 3NT
Tel: 01908 392299
Fax: 01908 392541
www.rajdhanimk.com
Restaurant/Take-away

FOODIE
Reader Comment

"The food is consistently good - I would recommend to everyone."
A.S.

"As featured on BBC's Look East"

The Rajdhani is a family owned restaurant and a popular place for visiting actors and actresses appearing at the nearby theatre, which speaks volumes for both their food and service.

Run by Ali, who regular diners will know is a very welcoming and knowledgeable host, you can expect an excellent dining experience.

Regularly rated in the top 100 Indian restaurants in the UK, which is not surprising considering how passionate and proud Ali is of his restaurant.

All dishes are freshly prepared, using whenever possible, locally sourced ingredients and none contain any artificial colourings.

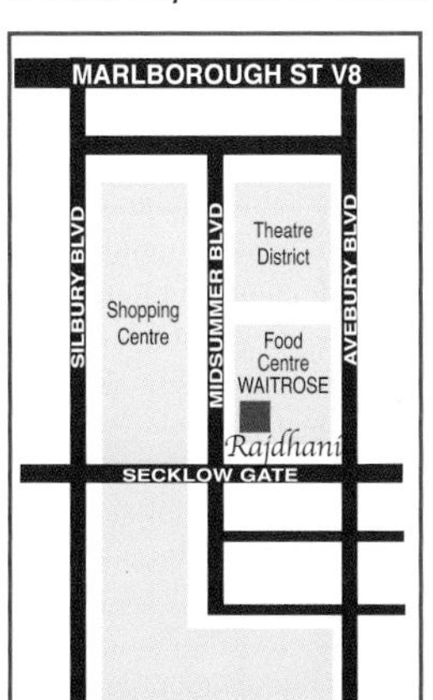

Ali's three chefs, work tirelessly in their immaculately clean kitchen, which has gained a four star rating for food hygiene by Environmental Health, preparing imaginative and tasty dishes which number a staggering 30 plus.

If you visit on a Sunday or Monday evening, which is when they hold their very popular buffets, you can choose from over 25 different dishes.

Want to eat in? – no problem there, as the Rajdhani offer a free home delivery service on orders over £12, or if you wish to collect it yourself Ali will give you 20% off on orders over £15 (excluding set menus and Thali dishes).

Why not take advantage of 25% off your total food bill when dining in the restaurant by using their Special Foodie Voucher? (see voucher for details).

Opening times: Open 7 days a week
Mon-Thur 12 noon - 2.30 pm & 6.00 pm - 11.00 pm
Fri 6.00 pm - 12 midnight
Sat 12 noon - 2.30 pm & 6.00 pm - 12 midnight
Sun 12 noon - 10.30 pm

DC

Prego

4 High Street
Buckingham
MK18 1NT
Tel: 01280 821205

8 St John's Street
Newport Pagnell
MK16 0EP
Tel: 01908 217535

Email: mail@pregorestaurants.com
www.pregorestaurants.com

Mediterranean style restaurant and wine bar. Prego meaning 'you're welcome' offers you Mediterranean food with typically relaxed and friendly service in a lively atmosphere.

Our Italian influenced menu caters for all times of the day or just visit for a coffee or a drink. We offer an extensive choice of food which apart from the vast range of traditional Italian pizzas and pasta, offers a fantastic choice of fresh chicken and seafood dishes alongside tasty vegetarian options.

But don't forget to leave room for our delicious Mediterranean desserts which include traditional Italian ice creams and sorbets. Children are always welcome and catered for with our excellent children's menu.

We look forward to seeing you.

FOODIE
Reader Comment

"Lovely food and atmosphere - was quite busy but only waited 10 minutes for a table"

G.H.

Opening times:
Mon-Sun All day from 11.00 am - 10.30 pm

The Vanilla Pod

31 West Street, Marlow, Buckinghamshire SL7 2LS
Tel: 01628 898101
Fax: 01628 898108
Email: contact@thevanillapod.co.uk
www.thevanillapod.co.uk

2010 Regional Winner of the Good Food Guide Reader's Restaurant Of The Year Award

The Vanilla Pod's discreet dining room is tucked away behind the elegant black door in Marlow's West Street. Once home to T.S. Eliot, one of the most distinguished literary figures of the 20th century, the elegant home has been transformed into a modern, stylish restaurant. Rich colours and clean lines give a contemporary and luxurious feel, reflecting the outstanding quality of the food. Sociably round tables with high backed chairs give a sense of privacy and spaciousness. Sophisticated air conditioning has also been installed to further enhance comfort. The kitchen is run under the watchful eye of Chef Proprietor Michael Macdonald, who uses local produce to inspire a creative and extensive menu changing frequently, which you can enjoy in the main dining room or upstairs in the T.S. Eliot private dining room.

The Vanilla Pod is fine dining in a beautiful location, where the professionalism of the service allows you to relax and enjoy your experience.

FOODIE
Reader Comment

"I am very lucky to live nearby. Foodies would travel a long way for this quality food." M.T.

Early Week Set Dinner Menu

please visit our website for details

Valid for dinner on Tuesday, Wednesday and Thursday for a maximum of 6 people. Menu offers 3 choices of starters, main courses and desserts and changes every week. Coffee and drinks are not included

Please quote "Foodie10" when booking your table

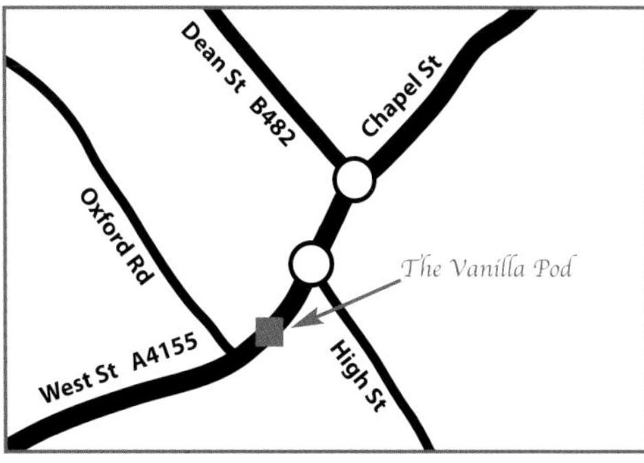

Food service times:
Tue-Sat 12 noon - 2.00 pm & 7.00 pm - 10.00 pm

Red Lion
COUNTRY HOTEL

Wavendon Road, Salford, Milton Keynes MK17 8AZ
Tel: 01908 583117
Email: info@redlionhotel.eu
www.redlionhotel.eu

FOODIE
Reader Comment
"Really worth visiting this pub - excellent food, wine and beer!" K.W.

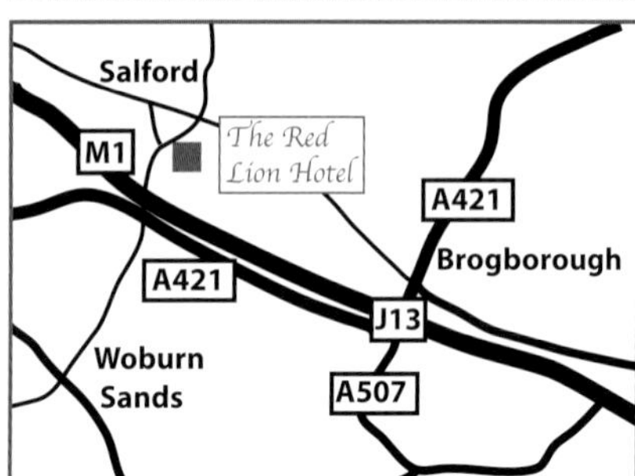

The Red Lion in Salford Village has been in the hands of Bob and Pauline Sapsford for 21 years and has in that time been a pub restaurant that has consistently delivered a friendly, traditional pub dining experience.

It's a traditional country inn with log fires, a huge beer garden and six letting rooms. Recently refurbished with a fresh new look but has managed to keep its cosy country pub feel.

The extensive menu has something to suit all tastes, occasions and budgets with top quality steak meals, seafood and chicken dishes alongside a great selection of light meals and snacks. There are spicy and classic dishes and a fair selection for vegetarians too. And for wine and ale lovers they have achieved 'Wine Pub of the Year' awards nationaly and locally with Charles Wells and have been in the Good Beer Guide for nearly 20 years.

Opening times:
Mon-Sun 12 noon - 2.00 pm & 6.15 pm - 9.30 pm

V £5

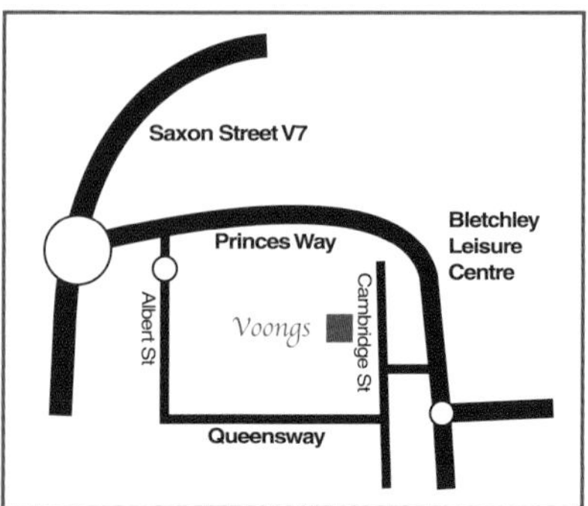

Voongs

1-2 Woodward House
Cambridge Street
Bletchley
MK2 2TH
Tel: 01908 370292

You must try it to believe it.

Opening times:
Mon Closed all day Monday except Bank Holidays
Tue-Sun 12 noon - 2.00 pm & 6.00 pm - 10.00 pm
Sun 12 noon - 2.00 pm (Special Buffet)

£5

FOODIE
Reader Comment

"This is my favourite Chinese - the food and service is second to none."
G.M.

9 Market Square
Old Amersham
Buckinghamshire
HP7 0DF
Tel: 01494 726611
www.artichokerestaurant.co.uk

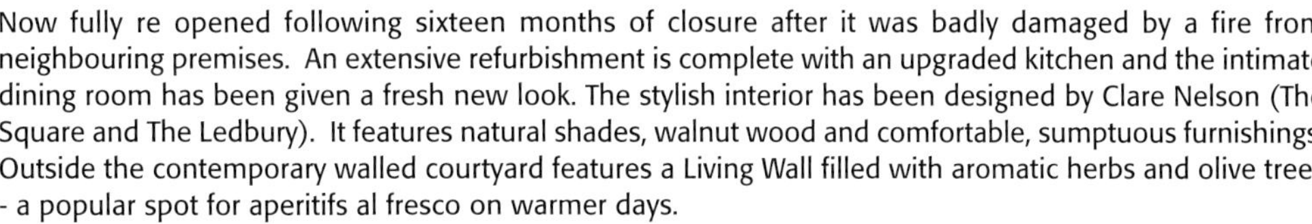

Now fully re opened following sixteen months of closure after it was badly damaged by a fire from neighbouring premises. An extensive refurbishment is complete with an upgraded kitchen and the intimate dining room has been given a fresh new look. The stylish interior has been designed by Clare Nelson (The Square and The Ledbury). It features natural shades, walnut wood and comfortable, sumptuous furnishings. Outside the contemporary walled courtyard features a Living Wall filled with aromatic herbs and olive trees - a popular spot for aperitifs al fresco on warmer days.

Set in the beautiful medieval town of Old Amersham just 35 minutes outside of London, Dorset born Laurie Gear opened The Artichoke in 2002 with his wife Jacqueline. His subtle, refined modern European cooking quickly garnered critical plaudits and the Artichoke was awarded UK Best Dish, Restaurant Magazine in 2007 and are delighted to be awarded the Best New Entry by the Good Food Guide 2011, a great achievement after just nine months of re opening.

The cuisine has an emphasis on the organic, free range, berries, herbs and fungi that can be foraged from our hedgerows, forests and seashores. Laurie has sourced a wonderful array of passionate suppliers, his mission to seek out the best produce that the British Isles have to offer and he has been delighted to find a collection of artisan producers right on his doorstep. The repertoire of menus include a gastronomic seven course tasting menu with wine pairing.

The Artichoke is great to discover as a neighbourhood restaurant or equally to visit for a special celebration.

FOODIE
Reader Comment

"An evening here is a very special event and one which you will want to repeat again and again." H.S.

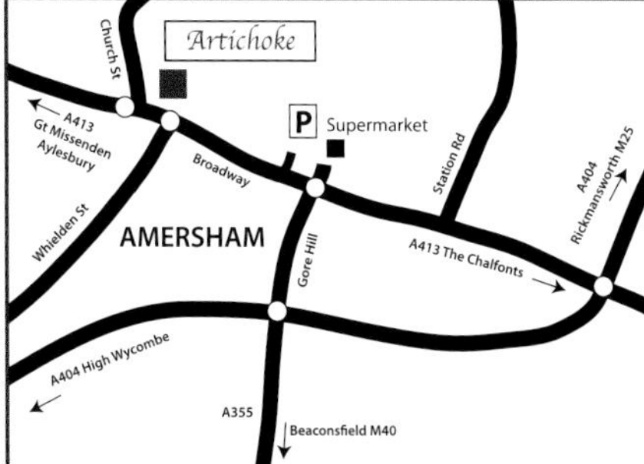

Food service times:
Mon Closed
Tue-Sat 12 noon - 2.30 pm & 6.30 pm - 11.00 pm
Sun Closed

The Swan Inn

Broughton Road
Milton Keynes Village
Milton Keynes
Buckinghamshire MK10 9AH
Tel: 01908 665240
Fax: 01908 395081
Email: info@theswan-mkvillage.co.uk
www.theswan-mkvillage.co.uk

This 13th Century thatched pub features flagstone floors, an open fire set in an inglenook fireplace and a sheltered orchard garden. Sympathetically renovated, the interior is an eclectic mix of traditional charm and contemporary chic with warm fabrics and clever use of natural finishes. The dining room overlooks a terrace set in the garden and is ideal for summer dining.

Real ales feature alongside an extensive wine list boasting over 20 wines by the glass and the range of soft drinks include a selection of organic fruit juices and lemonades. An open plan kitchen prepares a simple yet creative menu, changed monthly in line with the seasons, based on excellent value and local ingredients, including herbs from its own garden.

Sunday lunch is a traditional affair with a selection of succulent roasts and plentiful veg and potatoes. Daily changing specials plus a selection of lighter lunch items complete the food offer.

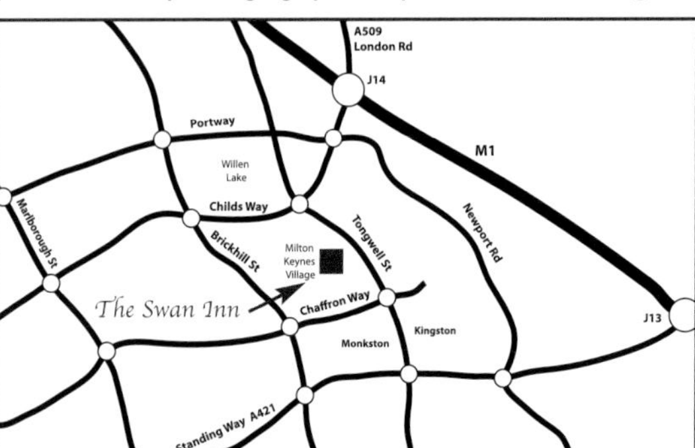

Service is brisk and friendly by the knowledgeable staff who herald from around the globe. The atmosphere is always lively given the core group of locals who support this warm and welcoming pub in the heart of the original Milton Keynes Village. A real find.

FOODIE
Reader Comment

"Great place for a special celebration or a meal for two. Excellent food and good service."
H.G.

Food service times:
Mon-Thur 12 noon - 3.00 pm & 6.00 pm - 9.30 pm
Fri-Sat 12 noon - 3.00 pm & 6.00 pm - 10.00 pm
Sun 12 noon - 6.00 pm

10%

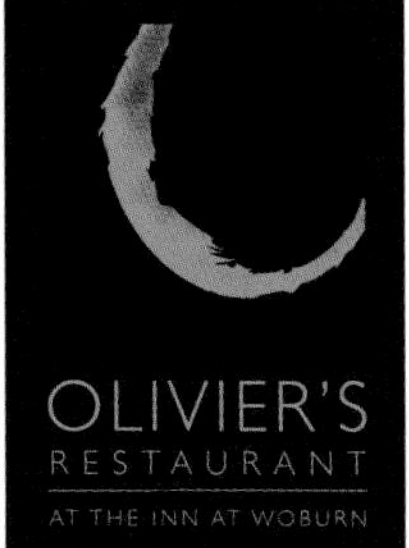

Two AA rosettes for fine food

George Street
Woburn
Bedfordshire
MK17 9PX
Tel: 01525 290441
Fax: 01525 290432
Email: inn@woburn.co.uk
www.woburn.co.uk/inn

FOODIE
Reader Comment

"I can't fault this restaurant, best for miles around!"

C.A.

Olivier's Restaurant at The Inn at Woburn offers a stylish and relaxed setting to enjoy the very best of English and continental dining.

Owned and managed by the historic Woburn estate, Olivier's Restaurant at The Inn at Woburn is situated in the heart of the Georgian village of Woburn.

With two AA Rosettes, the restaurant's reputation continues to flourish under the auspices of Head Chef Olivier Bertho who provides a superb menu of contemporary English and continental cuisine, all served with flair and imagination. An extensive and carefully selected wine list from around the globe perfectly complements the menus.

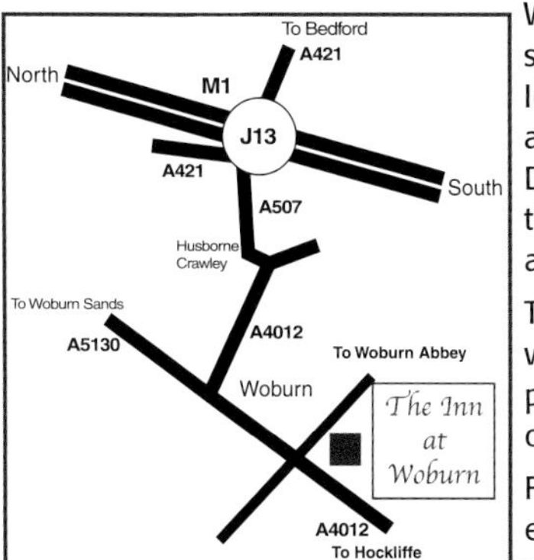

We also offer a range of daily specials and often celebrate special occasions with one-off dishes for lunch or dinner. In addition, we perpetuate the Woburn tradition of afternoon tea, which is said to have been started by Duchess Anna Maria, wife of the 7th Duke of Bedford in the 1840's when she served delicate sandwiches, cakes and biscuits in the Blue Drawing Room at Woburn Abbey.

The Tavistock bar and Lounge at The Inn provides a welcoming and comfortable spot to relax and linger with pre-dinner drinks or after dinner coffee to make the most of your visit.

For further details of our menus, wine list and dining events, please visit the Woburn estate website: www.woburn.co.uk/inn

Food service times:
Mon - Sat Lunch: 12 noon - 2.00 pm Dinner: 6.30 pm - 9.30 pm
Sun Lunch: 12.30 pm - 2.00 pm Dinner: 6.30 pm - 9.15 pm Afternoon Tea: 3.00 pm - 5.00 pm

Voucher valid Mon - Sat off à la carte only

Moreteyne Manor

Woburn Road
Marston Moreteyne
Bedfordshire
MK43 0NQ
Tel: 01234 767003
Email: dining@moreteynemanor.co.uk
www.moreteynemanor.co.uk

FOODIE
Reader Comment

"We had our wedding reception here, truly amazing venue. Food was lovely"

H.A.

Moreteyne Manor is a hidden treasure in the village of Marston Moreteyne, set amidst beautiful landscaped gardens surrounded by a moat this 16th Century country house is an exciting venue to discover. The Manor was acquired by chef Mark Hickman and his wife Jacqui in 1996 and over the years have built up a reputation of a warm, relaxing atmosphere and superb food.

The Manor offers a 30 cover restaurant and two function rooms. The Mulberry Room between 40 to 50 covers. The Betty Howe Suite a private dining room for 18 covers. Weddings are catered for from the romance of a few to the elegance of a marquee in the delightful gardens.

The à la carte menu is an exploration of the finest red and white meats, seafood and country fresh vegetables and an extensive wine list to complement. Quite simply, a journey into culinary perfection. Please visit our new website for more details.

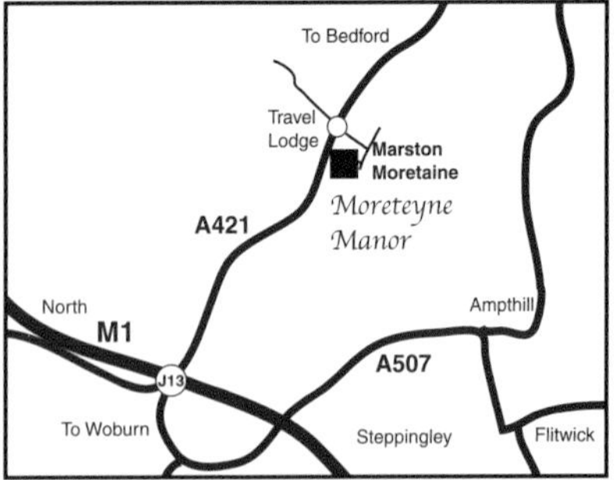

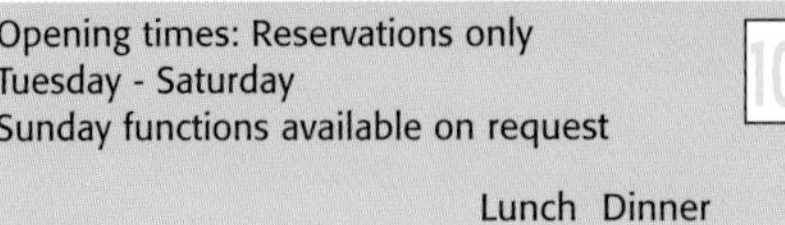

Opening times: Reservations only
Tuesday - Saturday
Sunday functions available on request

10%

The Waterfront Brasserie
Wyboston Lakes
Great North Road
Wyboston
Bedfordshire
MK44 3AL
Tel: 01480 212625
Email: brasserie@wybostonlakes.co.uk
www.thewaterfrontbrasserie.co.uk

FOODIE
Reader Comment

"Food was very good and the service was excellent." S.M.

Tucked away in 350 acres of rural countryside midway between Cambridge and Bedford, The Waterfront Brasserie, with its beautiful surroundings and lakeside vista, is synonymous with superb food and excellent levels of service.

Two of the region's most talented young hospitality professionals, chef Leigh Morris and restaurant manager Rickie Kitt, have joined culinary forces to oversee both front and back of house at The Waterfront Brasserie. Leigh's unique style combines the disciplines of French cuisine with today's savour-savvy palate, and fabulous new menus have been created which offer an eclectic mix of dishes using fresh seasonal produce, locally sourced wherever possible. In addition, a covetable wine list complements the Easy Eating Lounge Menu and Main Brasserie Menu.

As well as main courses, The Waterfront Brasserie offers a wide breakfast selection served throughout the day and the option of a speciality afternoon tea. Every Sunday a traditional British roast with all the trimmings is served from 12.00 pm with last orders at 3.30 pm.

For light and tasty bites, the Lounge is open from 7.00 am to 9.30 pm offering a symphony of 'All Day Easy Eating' options with American, Indian and Spanish influences. For those in a rush, speedy meals such as fried haddock and chips, burgers, pizzas, pastas, salads and sandwiches are available.

The Waterfront Brasserie can be taken at your own pace, so get together with colleagues, friends or family - whatever the occasion, and become part of the loyal following!

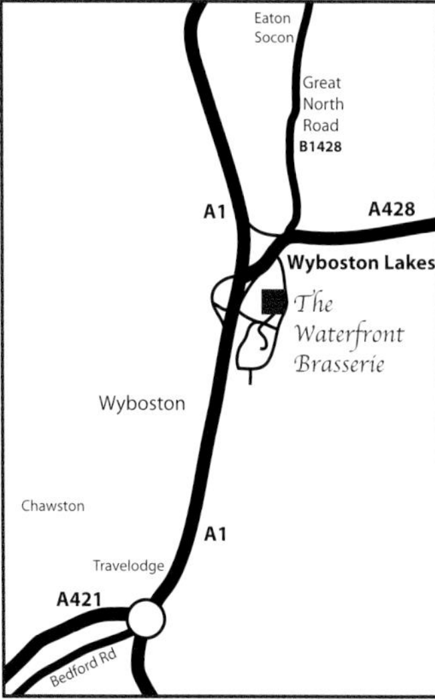

Food service times: **Mon-Sun** All Day Easy Eating Menu: 7.00 am - 9.30 pm
Brasserie Main Menu: 11.30 am - 3.00 pm & 6.30 pm - 9.30 pm
Sunday Lunch: 11.30 am - 3.30 pm Afternoon Tea: 3.00 pm - 6.00 pm

The Kings Head

Ivinghoe
Leighton Buzzard
Beds
LU7 9EB
Tel: 01296 668388
Fax: 01296 668107
Email: info@kingsheadivinghoe.co.uk
www.kingsheadivinghoe.co.uk

FOODIE
Reader Comment

"This is a wonderful restaurant if you enjoy high quality food in a traditional fine dining setting"

J.M.

The Kings Head is situated in the very heart of the picturesque village of Ivinghoe, on the Beds, Bucks and Herts borders. This ivy covered building dates back to times when quality and service went hand in hand and happily it still exists here to this day.

We pride ourselves on good old fashioned service and serious professionalism. Georges de Maison's passion for quality food, meticulous attention to detail and impeccable service ensures that your dining experience will be memorable if not unique. Soft candlelight and shimmering silverware complement the restaurants already inviting ambience.

Chef de Cuisine Jonathan O'Keeffe is famed for his skillfully prepared eclectic menus. Only the very best and freshest of produce is used with much of this sourced locally. After lunch or perhaps before dinner, why not take a stroll around the village and visit the windmill. If the weather is inclement take the opportunity sit back in one of our comfy chairs, order your favourite aperitif and let the world go by! Alternatively, take a few moments to explore over 50 original works of art which adorn the walls.

A Banqueting Suite is available for conferences and private dining for up to 40 guests. For larger functions and weddings, marquees can be put in the beautiful walled garden.

We promise a warm welcome and look forward to seeing you soon.

To Luton & Dunstable
To Leighton Buzzard
B488
The KingsHead
B489
Ivinghoe
Whipsnade
B489
A4146
A41(M)
B488
Tring
B4506
To Berkhamsted

Vouchers valid Mon-Thur for dinner only 10% DC

Food service times:
Mon-Sat 12 noon - 2.15 pm & 7.00 pm - 9.15 pm
Sun 12 noon - 2.15 pm

Cornfields Restaurant

Wilden Road, Colmworth, Beds MK44 2NJ
Tel: 01234 378990
Email: reservations@cornfieldsrestaurant.co.uk
www.cornfieldsrestaurant.co.uk

FOODIE
Reader Comment

"Food and service was very good. This a wonderful place to escape to." S.D.

A Breath of Fresh Air

A fresh food restaurant with five bedrooms located in peaceful countryside only fifteen minutes from Bedford town centre.

We offer traditional but non stuffy hospitality and service with a friendly enthusiastic hand picked team serving freshly prepared food from local producers where possible, cooked to order at sensible prices in an atmosphere that complements our food.

Our menus are constantly changing offering a varied and interesting selection of Fresh Fish, Meat, Game and Vegetarian choices.

Once a village inn, the main building dates back to the 17th century and is a Grade Two listed building which still retains its original oak beams and inglenook fireplace with bread oven. We have two dining rooms and a lounge with bar for pre or after dinner drinks. The larger of our dining rooms opens on to a private enclosed garden which, weather permitting, may be used to enjoy a drink or coffee. Either of our dining rooms can be used for small weddings, Private Functions or Conferences.

In addition to our Restaurant we have a choice of five spacious bedrooms set in our peaceful gardens. Each individually furnished offering a place to unwind and recharge after a busy day if on a business trip, or if on leisure to just relax with good food and hospitality.

We look forward to welcoming you.

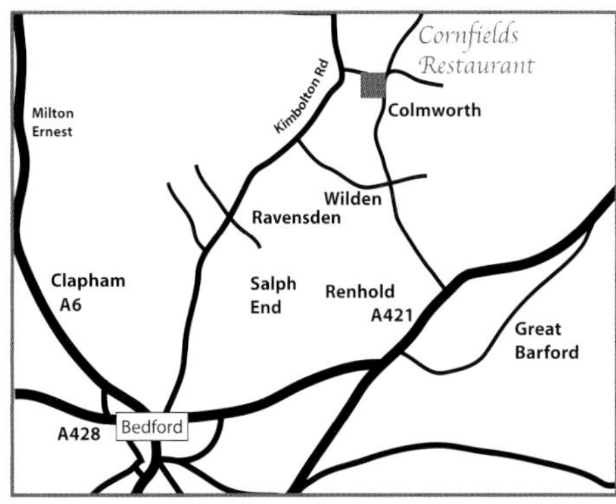

Food service times:
Mon-Sat 6.30 pm - 9.30 pm
Sun 12 noon - 1.45 pm

Galloway's

Aberdeen House
22-23 Market Place
Woburn
Bedfordshire
MK17 9PZ
Tel: 01525 290496
www.gallowayswoburn.com

FOODIE
Reader Comment

"Every course served to perfection. The wine was superb too. I would give this restaurant 10/10."

T.B.

'Party bookings and pre-booked lunches are welcomed'

Galloway's is a family run restaurant providing a relaxed informal atmosphere in a Grade II listed building in the heart of the historic village of Woburn.

Tuesday is our Pasta, Steak and Fish evening and Wednesday to Saturday we offer an à la carte menu which changes regularly, using only the best fresh produce. On Sunday we add our traditional roast selection to the menu for both lunchtime and evening service and we always have delicious vegetarian dishes. We are now open Friday lunchtimes too.

We will be celebrating our 15th Anniversary in November.

To Bedford
A421
North
M1
J13
A421
South
A507
Husborne Crawley
To Woburn Sands
A4012
A5130
Woburn
Galloway's
A4012
To A5
To Hockliffe

THE FOODIE AWARD 2009 Bedfordshire winner

Food service times:
Tue-Thur 6.30 pm - 10.00 pm
Fri 12 noon - 2.00 pm & 6.30 pm - 10.00 pm
Sat 6.30 pm - 10.00 pm
Sun 12 noon - 2.00 pm & 6.30 pm - 9.30 pm

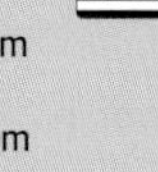

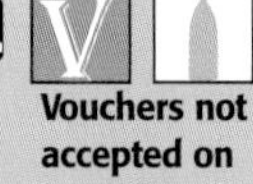

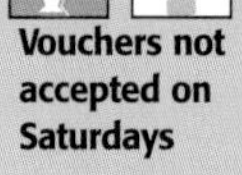

DC

Vouchers not accepted on Saturdays

FT

ST. HELENA RESTAURANT

High Street, Elstow
Bedfordshire
MK42 9XP
Tel: 01234 344848
www.sthelenarestaurant.com

FOODIE
Reader Comment

"If you enjoy good service, well prepared food in nice surroundings at reasonable prices, this is for you. Somewhere to go for that special occasion. A class act which in my view will be hard to beat." S.D.

Just a short drive from the A6 on the outskirts of Bedford is the small village of Elstow. In a secluded setting tucked behind a beautiful walled garden, you will find a 16th century private house which has been transformed to create St Helena Restaurant.

With style, elegance and a country home feeling of Englishness, it is home to a wonderful collection of antiques and fine paintings which makes it perfect to celebrate a special occasion, entertain important business clients or just an informal evening.

Brothers-in-law Raffaele and Franco offer an interesting and well prepared modern classic menu with Italian and French influence, accompanied by an excellent selection of fine and rare wines on a list of over 300 bins! In the winter the fires roar and in the summer a drink in the garden or near the pond precedes lunch or dinner perhaps in the new conservatory or one of the three elegant dining rooms. What was the bar/sitting room is now an elegant dining room giving extra seating, making last minute bookings easier to accommodate.

Fresh seafood including Cornish Lobster, Crab and Oysters from Bigbury Bay are available regularly as well as quality Scottish and English Lamb and Beef, Rare Breed Pork and local Game. Classic dishes with a twist can often be found on what is always a good choice menu, along with such regulars as Brie & Rosemary Soufflé, Tiger King Prawns pan fried with Chilli and Garlic and Homemade Chilli Jam or St Helena Fillet of Beef stuffed with Stilton on a Madeira Sauce.

For a full menu please see the website www.sthelenarestaurant.com.

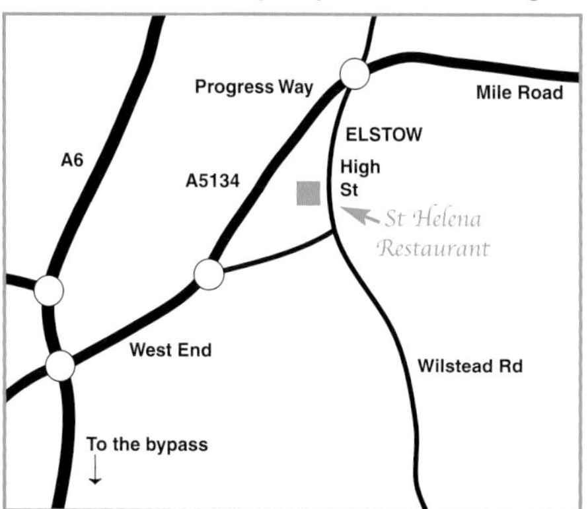

Food service times:
Sunday & Monday Closed all day
Tue 7.00 pm - 9.00 pm (last orders)
Wed-Fri 12.15 pm - 1.00 pm (last orders) & 7.00 pm - 9.00 pm (last orders)
Sat 7.00 pm - 9.00 pm (last orders)

lunch

dinner

Horse & Jockey

Church End
Ravensden
Bedford
MK44 2RR
Tel: 01234 772319
Email: horseandjockey@live.com
www.horseandjockey.info

FOODIE
Reader Comment

"Go and find this place, great food and lovely garden." J.K.

Only 5 minutes from Bedford yet in the heart of the countryside the Horse and Jockey at Church End, Ravensden is well worth a visit. Situated next to the beautiful old church of All Saints amidst thatched cottages it is an ideal place to unwind.

Recently taken over by Darron & Sarah Smith it has been completely restyled and now offers a wonderful atmosphere both as a pub and restaurant. Indoors or out there is the chance to relax. Whether you come just for a drink and one of Darron's locally famous snack pots or to dine in the restaurant you will not be disappointed.

This freehouse offers a range of beers and guest ales as well as an extensive wine list and a menu of freshly prepared high quality ever changing dishes. Chef Darron strongly believes in using the best quality ingredients with an emphasis on supporting local producers. The menu includes a great variety of game dishes when in season as well as a broad range of classics including Darron's signature dish of Belly Pork. In addition he also has an excellent fish menu that changes daily dependent on catch.

Darron and Sarah, with their welcoming staff, have created a venue with friendly atmosphere, excellent service and quality food at affordable prices.

Food service times:
Mon-Thur 12 noon - 2.00 pm & 6.00 pm - 9.00 pm
Fri-Sat 12 noon - 2.00 pm & 6.00 pm - 9.30 pm
Sun 12 noon - 7.00 pm

The Prince of Wales

24 Bedford Street, Ampthill, Bedfordshire MK45 2NB
Tel: 01525 840504
Fax: 01525 840574
Email: ricksbar1@aol.com
www.princeofwales-ampthill.com

FOODIE
Reader Comment

"We were delighted with the quality of food and found the atmosphere relaxed and informal."
T.B.

Welcome to the Prince of Wales, where freshly prepared quality food and wines meets informality and a relaxing atmosphere in a unique but comfortable setting. The Prince of Wales is a traditional red brick town inn, where the emphasis is on hospitality - from the welcoming ambience and the attentive service to the quality of the dining experience. Lovingly refurbished, The Prince of Wales delights with its individually designed surroundings and consideration to detail. Fresh flowers, new oak and flagstone flooring throughout combine to make the perfect setting to relax over coffee or drinks, have lunch or dinner, or enjoy al fresco dining in the garden. Recently renovated and refurbished, the 5 individually designed en-suite bedrooms provide a welcoming retreat making for an even more enjoyable stay!

The award winning Prince of Wales has now been included nationally in The Good Pub Guide for the past 3 years including 2011. We pride ourselves on only using the finest locally sourced produce which is lovingly prepared daily by our team of experienced chefs. Monday to Saturday lunchtimes we offer an extensive 'Lite Bite' menu with dishes from £5, including jackets, salads, baguettes, wraps and hand cut sandwiches. Main courses from £7 to £15: beer battered Grimsby cod fillet, homemade steak burger, meat loaf, homemade pie of the day, homemade chips - to mention a few! Monday to Thursday evening our mid week special offer "Four Seasons Menu' using only the finest locally sourced seasonal produce. Menus are changed weekly, great value at 2 courses: £15 and 3 courses: £20. Friday and Saturday evenings we serve our full à la carte menu offering a wide and varied selection of freshly produced modern British cuisine. Finishing the week with our famous Sunday lunch, cooked from fresh each week with a seletion of four roasts, a selection of starters and desserts at only 2 courses: £15 and 3 courses: £17.

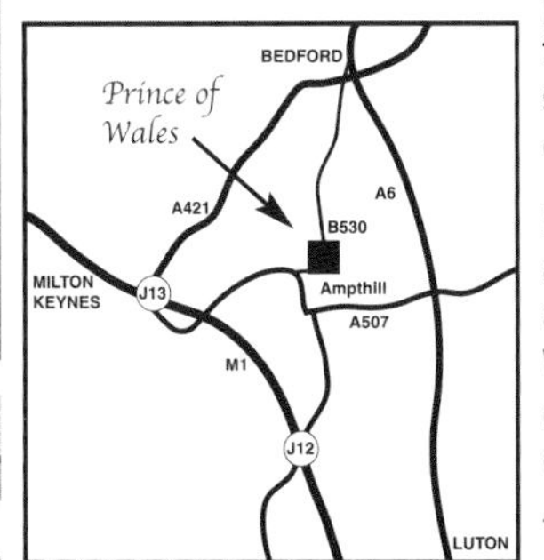

Families with children are welcome at any time of the week and depending on what they eat we charge accordingly. Food allergies are taken very seriously by the chefs at The Prince of Wales, we can cater for gluten, nut and lactose free. Please advise us upon booking and we will accommodate all your dietary requirements.

The Prince of Wales has the perfect atmosphere for every occasion. Private parties of up to 100 people are catered for, the restaurant is ideal for wedding receptions, banquets, parties or any special occasion. Alternatively, we also offer outside catering.

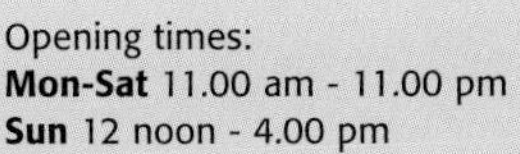

Opening times:
Mon-Sat 11.00 am - 11.00 pm
Sun 12 noon - 4.00 pm

Vouchers valid Friday and Saturday evenings only

Church End
Eversholt
Milton Keynes MK17 9DU
Tel: 01525 288111
Email: info@greenmaneversholt.com
www.greenmaneversholt.com

FOODIE
Reader Comment

"Sunday lunch was gorgeous, tender meat, stunning roast potatoes. Real quality food." J.Y.

Tucked away in one of England's prettiest villages, Eversholt just outside of Woburn, is The Green Man Pub and Restaurant. Owned and run by James and Louise Freeman, this pub is becoming known as a "Hidden Gem".

Now a freehouse, it was refurbished throughout in October 2008. The Green Man has carefully retained the charm of a local pub whilst bringing it into the 21st Century.

The refurbishment uncovered fireplaces that were previously boarded up and created an intimate restaurant tucked away from the bar area and overlooking the cricket pitch and church.

The menu demonstrates their philosophy of "Traditional with a twist". Chef James creates classic dishes all made from scratch – from the Roast Ham & Free Range Eggs to Salmon & Crayfish Fishcakes. The specials board often features fresh fish including Scallops & Black Pudding to Beer Battered Fish & Chips. Watch out for Sunday Roast – it is hard to be beaten!

James also offers outside catering as "The Hogman". He can cater for your special event either at The Green Man or a location of your choice. Offering freshly cooked Pig or Lamb Roast, all sourced locally, plus side salads and even a Real Ale bar!

With a large patio garden, James & Louise look forward to welcoming new and old customers to sample the ales, enjoy the wines and taste the menu.

Woburn
Eversholt
Hill's End
Church End
Tingrith
Little Brickhill
A4012
A5
The Green Man
Milton Bryan
Great Brickhill
Potsgrove
Toddington
Heath and Reach
Hockliffe

10% Voucher valid only for tables up to 6 people

£5 10%

Food served times:
Mon 7.00 pm - 9.00 pm
Tue-Thur 12 noon - 2.00 pm & 7.00 pm - 9.00 pm
Fri 12 noon - 2.00 pm & 6.30 pm - 9.00 pm
Sat 12 noon - 2.30 pm & 6.30 pm - 9.00 pm
Sun 12 noon - 3.00 pm

Brook Lane, Flitton, Beds MK45 5EJ
Tel: 01525 862022
Email: philhale@btconnect.com
www.whitehartflitton.co.uk

FOODIE
Reader Comment

"Fresh succulent scallops followed by fresh fish cooked to perfection. Would definitely recommend" S.D.

In the picturesque village of Flitton, nestled between the beautiful St John the Baptist church and Flitton Moor you will find the picture postcard setting of the White Hart.

With everything you would expect from a village pub, including bar snacks and real ales, to the unexpected offerings of fresh fish, fine wines and as a member of the Scotch Beef Club a chance to tackle one of our Aberdeen Angus steaks. Open for lunch and dinner Tuesday to Saturday and a traditional lunch on Sunday, our experienced team in the kitchen offer fresh food, sourced locally where possible, with the emphasis on doing things 'simply but properly'.

From wine tasting evenings to quiz nights and Mausoleum tours in the St John the Baptist Church to Bank Holiday Hog Roasts the White Hart offers something for everyone so keep yourself up to date at www.whitehartflitton.co.uk and join our mailing list.

Our beautiful setting gives us the facility and capacity to host a range of celebrations and events either within our pub or in a marquee in our grounds. Whether you are looking for that country pub lunch, quiet dinner for two or a celebration with 200 of your friends and family, you imagine it and through our experience the White Hart will help you achieve it.

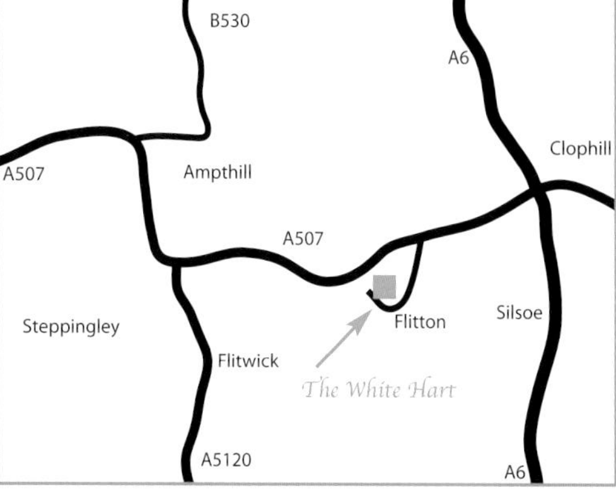

DC

Food service times:
Tue-Thur 12 noon - 2.00 pm & 7.00 pm - 9.00 pm
Fri-Sat 12 noon- 2.00 pm & 6.30 pm - 9.30 pm
Sun 12 noon - 3.00 pm

Hog Pits Bottom
Flaunden
Hemel Hempstead HP3 0PH
Tel: 01442 833322
Email: goodfood@bricklayersarms.com
www.bricklayersarms.com

"Hertfordshire's Restaurant of the Year 2006, 2009 & 2010" – The Foodie Guide
"Dining Pub of The Year" – The Good Pub Guide 2009
Michelin Guide 2009
"Commendation Award 2009" – Harden's Guide
Claude Paillet "Chef of the Year Award" – The Publican Food Award
"Freehouse of The Year" – The Morning Advertiser
"Food Pub of The Year" - The Publican Magazine

"This is a foodies delight - really lovely food, freshly prepared and flavoursome." K.H.

The Bricklayers Arms is an 18th century, ivy clad and flint built listed building, tucked away in the tiny Hertfordshire village of Flaunden which can be found at the end of the winding lanes that snake between Chipperfield and Latimer.

A picturesque pub in a beautiful location often featured in film and tv series. You are sure to receive a warm welcome from one of the Michaels family where you can enjoy the atmosphere with the pubs low wooden beams and real log fire.

Over the past five years, The Bricklayers Arms has certainly gained an excellent reputation for its English traditional and French Fusion menu created by its award winning chef, Claude Paillet. You can enjoy the same menu throughout the restaurant and pub seven days a week with dishes ranging at lunchtime from their famous smoked fish plate (all smoked on the premises), home made terrines to their traditional cod in Tring ale batter; 21 day aged fillet Steaks and local fillet of pork bred from Worcestershire black spotted pigs.

You'll always find a selection of fresh fish dishes and vegetarian options on the menu.

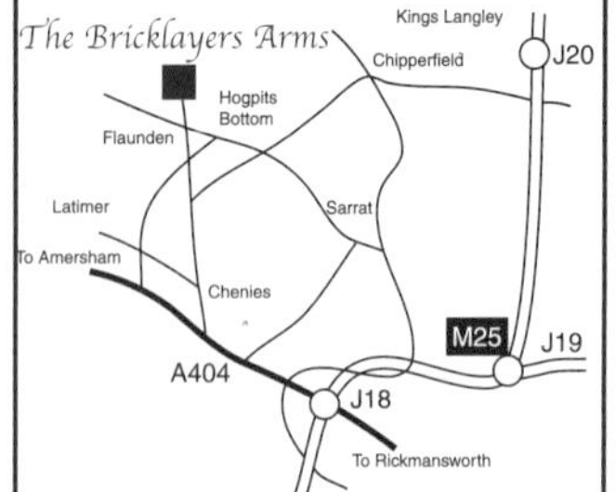

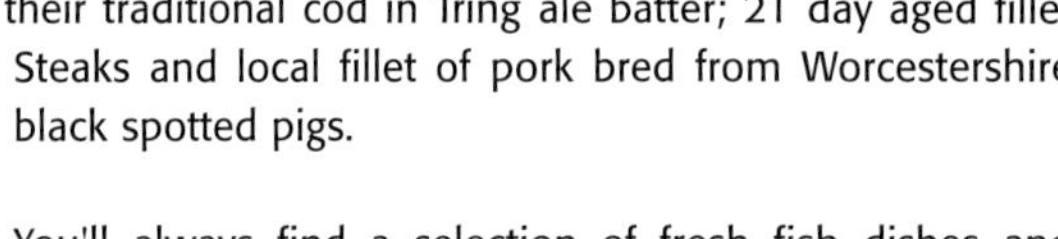
Food service times:
Mon-Sat 12 noon - 2.30 pm & 6.30 pm - 9.30 pm
Sun 12 noon - 3.30 pm & 6.30 pm - 8.30 pm
£5

20 Green End
Braughing
Hertfordshire
SG11 2PG
Tel: 01920 823555
Email: pub@goldenfleecebraughing.co.uk
www.goldenfleecebraughing.co.uk

FOODIE
Reader Comment

"Lovely welcome and great food, would definitely go back."
L.P.

Jess and Peter Tatlow, the new owners of The Golden Fleece, would like to welcome you to a new era in the pub's long history. Having successfully run the George & Dragon at Watton-at-Stone for 9 years they intend to bring to Braughing the same quality of food, service and ambience.

The building dates back to the 17th century so, as you would expect, there are oak beams, exposed brickwork and open fireplaces to welcome you. The comfortable and convivial bar is an ideal spot to meet friends and enjoy a pint, or read the papers over a coffee or a glass of wine. You can also choose from a menu of freshly prepared food made from locally sourced products. In the winter you can be sure of a roaring log fire to warm the cockles of your heart - and your hands of course.

Food is served in the main dining room, private dining room, pub bar and outside on the newly completed terraces. Tables can be reserved in both dining rooms. There are a range of dishes on offer all prepared in their own kitchen, using only the freshest ingredients and wherever possible, these are sourced from local suppliers.

"Creating new and exciting dishes from local produce is both challenging and a lot of fun. We just love seeing our customers satisfied and contented. Our goal is to exceed our customers' expectations and, to that end, our friendly staff - some of whom came with us from Watton - are well-trained and informed about the food and drinks they serve, including special dietary requirements. We are passionate about our food, wines and ales so we always aim to go that extra mile to make every dining experience a special occasion. We look forward to welcoming customers old and new for many years to come."

Food service times:
Mon-Thur 12 noon - 2.30 pm & 6.30 pm - 9.00 pm
Fri-Sat 12 noon - 2.30 pm & 6.30 pm - 10.00 pm
Sun 12 noon - 6.00 pm

CHEZ MUMTAJ

Modern French-Asian Dining

Restaurant & Saffron Lounge Champagne Bar

136-142 London Road
St Albans
Hertfordshire
AL1 1PQ
Tel: 01727 800033
Email: info@chezmumtaj.com
www.chezmumtaj.com

FOODIE
Reader Comment

"Avant-garde menus in an incredible setting." R.C.

Chez Mumtaj is designed to impart the essence of stunning French and Asian cuisine, showcasing evolved modern dishes from India, France, Thailand, China and Malaysia for the discerning palate. The philosophy at Chez Mumtaj is to be innovative, progressive, persistent and passionate with cuisine and service.

Award winning Executive Chef Chad Rahman has created an eclectic menu depicting a diversity of traditional dishes with a contemporary twist. The menu encompasses a wide range of tastes and flavours journeying through South East Asia and Europe incorporating nuances of Pan Asian and European cuisines. Menus change regularly using only the finest and freshest seasonal ingredients.

For private or corporate events of 8 to 16 guests, there is a private dining room. They can co-ordinate and create a menu to suit your requirements so that the event is successful, bringing attention to detail, care and hospitality. The aim is to create a unique and memorable experience, tailored to your needs.

The Saffron Lounge offers an ideal space for pre-luncheon and dinner drinks and an Asian Tapas Bar Food Menu. The lounge can accommodate up to 28 guests seated and 50 for cocktails. The Saffron Lounge echoes many of the charming characteristics of the restaurant with rich mahogany panelled walls, luxurious leather banquette seating and antique mirror-panelled walls and in-built booths for privacy.

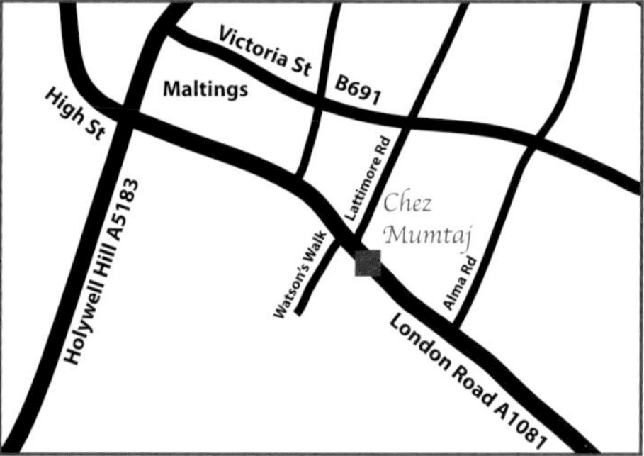

Food service times:
Tue-Sun 12 noon - 2.30 pm & 6.00 pm - 11.00 pm
The Saffron Lounge opening times:
Tue-Sun 6.00 pm - 11.00 pm

Doughty's Brasserie

87 Bancroft
Hitchin
Herts SG5 1NQ
Tel: 01462 456363
Email: enquiries@doughtysbrasserie.com
www.doughtysbrasserie.com

Also at
Doughty's at GL-14
Fairfield Hall
Hitchin Road
Stotfold
Beds SG5 4JJ
Tel: 01462 835525

Doughty's Brasserie offers a sophisticated and relaxed dining experience in the heart of Hitchin's vibrant town centre and at Fairfield Park in Stotfold for lunch, brunch or an evening meal. Both restaurants are situated in fantastic listed buildings which have both been lovingly restored after years of neglect and they exude a warmth and personality all of their own.

We are committed to using only the finest seasonal produce prepared with a simplicity that will delight even the most discerning of tastes. We hope there is something for everyone, whether you are out for a snack or a special occasion.

Doughty's Brasserie is ideal for the casual visitor, business lunches or evening functions. We can cater for up to 60 guests in the restaurants for events and we tailor all our menus totally to your personal requirements.

Watch the world go by over a cup of coffee or spend a delightful evening with friends or loved ones in comfort. We are delighted to welcome returning guests but love to see new faces too.

Doughty's Brasserie prepares all types of cuisine with that special twist of subtle seasoning that is lovingly and freshly prepared and cooked to perfection.

FOODIE
Reader Comment

"Brilliant food, atmosphere and not expensive"
J. W.

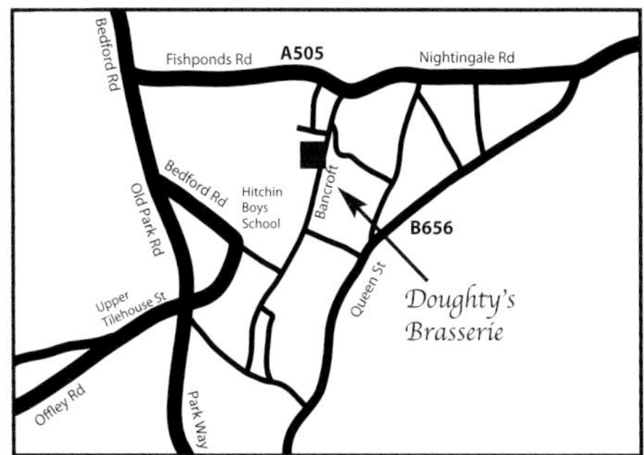

Opening times:
Mon Closed
Tue-Sat 11.00 am - 3.30 pm
& 6.30 pm - midnight
Sun Closed

Doughty's at GL-14:
Open 7 days a week all day, closed Sunday nights

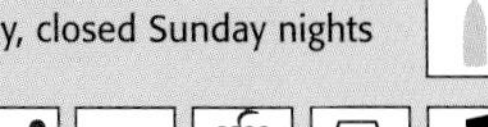

The Fox & Hounds

2 High Street
Hunsdon
Ware
Hertfordshire
SG12 8NH
Tel: 01279 843999
Fax: 01279 841092
Email: info@foxandhounds-hunsdon.co.uk
www.foxandhounds-hunsdon.co.uk

FOODIE
Reader Comment

"Not easy to find but worth the effort. Good food and nice atmosphere."

P.M.

The Fox & Hounds is a family run establishment in the pretty village of Hunsdon. Now in its fifth year, it is established as one of Hertfordshire's leading gastro pubs, receiving impressive reviews and accolades in numerous press articles and guides. Chef/proprietor James Rix has previously worked in some of London's most celebrated eateries.

Everything is made in-house and the menu changes daily making the best of good quality seasonal produce. Rare breed meats and locally shot game feature and shellfish is delivered daily from the East and South coasts. Sample dishes include Rabbit Livers, Asparagus & Soft Boiled Egg, Terrine Chutney and Toast and Smoked Eel, Potato Pancake, Beetroot and Horseradish. For main course why not try the popular Cote de Boeuf, Sauce Béarnaise and Hand Cut Chips or 'Label Anglais' Chicken, Peas, Morels and Broad Beans. Finish off with Bitter Chocolate Tart and Espresso Ice Cream. There is an interesting wine list with a good selection offered by the glass or carafe.

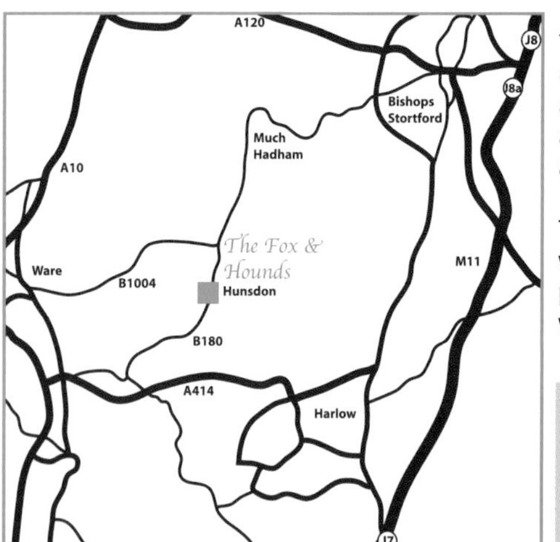

The pub has a friendly, informal atmosphere with a comfy laid back bar, log fire, leather sofas and local ales. The homely dining room features a chandelier and is popular for gatherings of families and friends and for private functions.

The large garden comes into its own in the summer with a large covered/heated patio and children's play area - great to keep the children entertained whilst having a quiet drink or bite to eat.

Food service times:
Tue - Sat 12 noon - 3.00 pm & 6.30 pm - 10.00 pm
Sun 12 noon - 3.00 pm

Ayot St Peter
To Wheathampstead
Welwyn Garden City
B653
AI(M)
J5
Auberge du Lac
Cromer Hyde
A6129
Stanborough
J4
A414

Auberge du Lac

Brocket Hall
Welwyn
Hertfordshire AL8 7XG
Tel: 01707 368888
Fax: 01707 368898
Email: aubergeevents@brocket-hall.co.uk
www.aubergedulac.co.uk

Auberge du Lac is set in the magnificent parkland of Brocket Hall and promises to uphold the finest culinary standards to further enhance Brocket Hall's international reputation for excellence.

A former Hunting Lodge dating back to 1760, Auberge du Lac sits proudly alongside the water's edge in its own peaceful environment, overlooking the splendour of the Estate. Timeless elegance will surround you, enabling you to relax and enjoy the fine wines and superb dishes.

Auberge du Lac provides a culinary delight in this most beautiful setting, yet only 40 minutes from central London.

Food service times:
Sunday & Monday Closed
Tue-Sat Lunch: 12 noon - 2.30 pm
Dinner: 7.00 pm - 9.30 pm

High Street, Reed, Royston, Hertfordshire SG8 8AH
Tel: 01763 848366 **Email:** thecabinet@btconnect.com
www.thecabinetatreed.co.uk

A beautifully preserved 16th Century Inn and restaurant with low beamed ceilings, a cosy fireplace, serene country setting and a welcoming pint of real ale; The Cabinet is a place most people think only exists in novels.

Angus Martin (formally executive chef at Fortnum and Mason) is driving the kitchen and provenance of the food; locally sourced if possible. Tracey Hale, former Cambridge restaurateur, keeps a keen eye on service and all wine matters (supplied by friend and fellow foodie Paul Bowes of "Bacchanalia").

The menu changes monthly to take advantage of the best produce available. On offer is an award winning mix of menus from an easy and relaxed supper menu to the fast and punchy Snug and Bar menu featuring all your favorite pub meals, also Sunday lunch for those in search of a traditional roast.

Food service times:
Tue-Sat 12 noon - 3.00 pm & 6.00 pm - 9.00 pm
Sun 12 noon - 3.00 pm

100 High Street, Paulerspury
Northamptonshire, NN12 7NA
Tel: 01327 811267
Fax: 01327 811309
Email: info@vinehousehotel.com
www.vinehousehotel.com

FOODIE
Reader Comment

"If you desire something special then this is where you will find it" S.D.

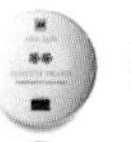

Proprietors, chef and host Marcus & Julie Springett are devoted to their 300 year old Northamptonshire stone Vine House Hotel & Restaurant in Paulerspury and have attained a multi award winning reputation for offering outstanding cuisine and a warm personal welcome for all their guests.

The restaurant is open year round attracting diners both local and from far and wide on a satisfied quest for the best outside of London, providing a fusion of traditional English and modern continental cuisine with a twist.

Located on the doorstep of Silverstone Race Circuit and Towcester for Horseracing it is handy for sporting fixtures thus frequented by participants and enthusiasts as well as visitors on shopping sprees to nearby Milton Keynes or Bicester Village. Others come for a stop-over change of scene, or celebration without the drive home. This top notch restaurant with individual rooms, named after famous wine making grapes and bedecked with antiques plus every modern facility, sets The Vine House apart from any hostelry in the region.

Choose alfresco summer eating in the unique Garden Folly or cosy fireside cream teas in the aqua lounge bar, or lunch or dinner in the 33 cover dining room from a daily changed menu that never fails to delight even the most regular visitor. Out of this world chocolates round off a meal, devotedly made on the premises by Chef Marcus as well as ice creams and breads. Indeed all dishes are from locally sourced ingredients, rare breed meats and interesting marriages of flavours that excite the taste buds.

From only £29.95 for 3 courses, £26.95 for 2 courses per head, expect informal dining with linen table cloths and award winning food to Fine Dining standard.

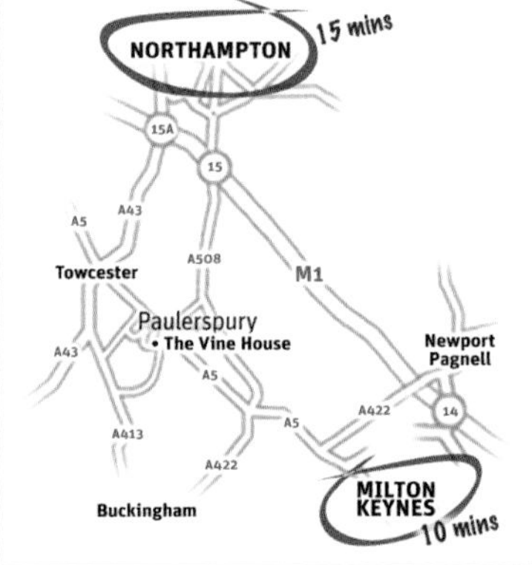

Food service times:
Lunch **Tue-Sat** 12.30 pm - 1.45 pm
Dinner **Mon-Sun** 6.30 pm - 10.00 pm
Special openings on Sunday for events and stopovers / residents

£5

Murrays

AT WHITTLEBURY HALL

Whittlebury Hall Hotel & Spa
Whittlebury
Nr Towcester
Northants
NN12 8QH
Tel: 01327 857857
Fax: 01327 857867
Email: reservations@whittleburyhall.co.uk
www.whittleburyhall.co.uk

Two AA rosettes for fine food

When you have a passion for food...
Murrays is a must, boasting 2 AA Rosettes for its fine cuisine.

Murrays provides a relaxing venue to enjoy the creative dishes presented by our award winning Chef and his brigade.

Steamed Fillet of Brill with a Crab and Herb Crust, Wilted Little Gems and Chervil Cream

With an ever increasing interest in food the Murrays menu, which changes regularly, provides our guests with the perfect opportunity to taste the latest blends of flavours and ingredients to make your visit to Murrays at Whittlebury Hall truly memorable.

Our philosophy is quite simple; cook the finest carefully sourced seasonal ingredients and simply add our own twists and innovations. Our Head Chef, Christian Morris, has spent many years working both in this country and around the world to bring you these dishes. Some are new discoveries and others are like old friends. Our style could be described as modern British with influences from international and classical based cookery. All food, from the appetisers to the desserts are produced in-house from carefully created recipes, no dish is left to chance.

Whilst relaxing in the lounge and during dinner you can reminisce on the F1 commentary years of Murray Walker as we display a collection of photographs with F1 celebrities and also display some unique anecdotes of his memorable career.

Dark Chocolate Fondant with Chocolate Macaroon and Pistachio Parfait

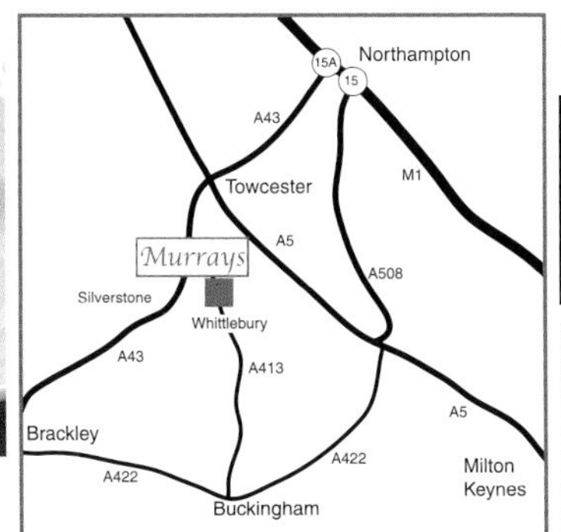

For more details go to www.whittleburyhall.co.uk/murrays or to book your fine dining experience call 0845 400 0001.

"The service was impeccable, the surroundings subtle and the food was out of this world." L.F.

Food service times:
Tue - Sat 7.00 pm - 9.45 pm

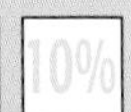

Roade House

restaurant & hotel

16 High Street
Roade
Northants
NN7 2NW
Tel: 01604 863372
Fax: 01604 862421
Email: info@roadehousehotel.co.uk
www.roadehousehotel.co.uk

FOODIE
Reader Comment

"The dining here is superb and in a very relaxed atmosphere."

P.T.

The Roade House restaurant has been owned by Chris and Sue Kewley for nearly 27 years. For most of that time it has been listed in The Good Food Guide as well as the Michelin, Harden and AA Restaurant Guides.

The building was originally a local village pub, The White Hart before it was converted into a restaurant. In 1997 an adjoining cottage was incorporated to create 10 guest bedrooms. Sue runs front of house and Chris is in charge of the kitchen.

Although the menu is small it is made using fresh, top quality and predominantly seasonal ingredients cooked to order. The Roade House provides an informal and relaxed atmosphere.

In addition to being an excellent venue for romantic dinners, business meetings or just a casual night out, a wide variety of functions are also catered for, from weddings to Golden wedding anniversaries, significant birthdays, retirement dinners and so on. Their extensive experience of organising and running functions means they are happy to produce tailored menus and for larger events offer exclusive use of the premises.

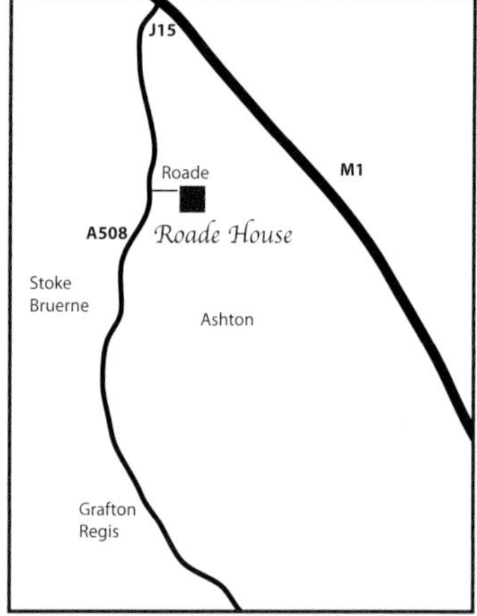

Food service times:
Mon-Fri 12.30 pm - 1.45 pm & 7.00 pm - 9.30 pm
Sat 7.00 pm - 9.30 pm
Sun 12 noon - 2.00 pm

The Wollaston Inn

87 London Road
Wollaston
Northants
NN29 7QS
Tel: 01933 663161
Email: info@wollaston-inn.co.uk
www.wollaston-inn.co.uk

FOODIE
Reader Comment

"The food is impeccable. Fresh ingredients prepared to a high standard. Tasty wine list too."
J. O.

Situated in the Village of Wollaston on the borders of Northamptonshire, Bedfordshire and Buckinghamshire the 350 year old Wollaston Inn has been revitalised in the past 7 years by Chef/Patron Chris Spencer.

With a passion for seafood and inspired by fresh, seasonal, regional food the restaurant offers a variety of food throughout the day. Both the evening à la carte and lunch menus offer the best of traditional British dishes alongside some classic Mediterranean and internationally influenced choices. Running alongside these is the daily changing fresh seafood menu using produce delivered daily from fish markets around Britain. On Sundays there is a traditional Sunday roast lunch and, like every other day food is served at all times throughout the day.

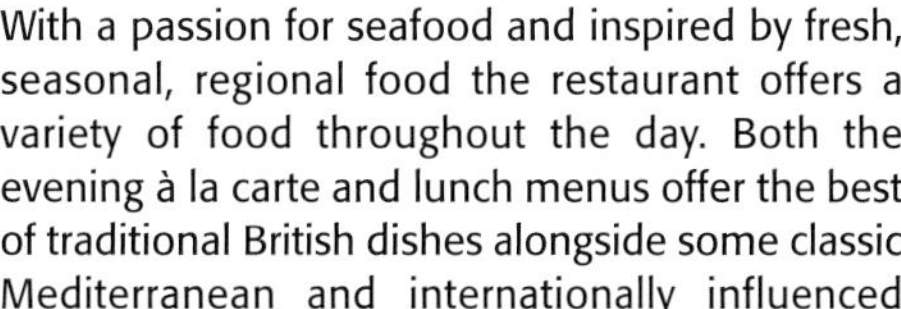

There are plenty of choices of places to eat - there is a main restaurant with an open fire roaring through the winter, in the summer you can walk out through the french doors and sit out on the sun drenched patio, the bar is available for a casual lunch or just enjoy a coffee relaxing on the Italian leather sofas. There are also two additional rooms that are ideal for family gatherings, business meetings or small social events.

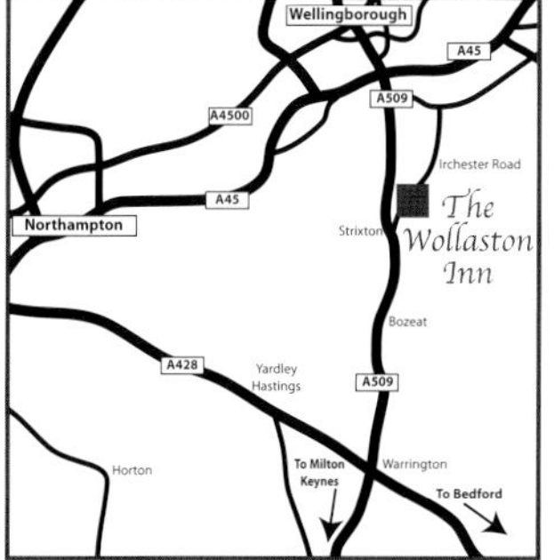

As well as the two private dining rooms there is the spacious function room available for weddings, celebrations and business meetings. With over 20 years of experience within the industry Chris can offer you bespoke menus and a personal service that few other venues can match.

Food service times:
Mon-Sat 11.00 am - 10.00 pm
Sun 12 noon - 9.30 pm

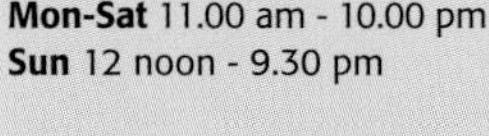

THE OLD CROWN

1 Stoke Road
Ashton
Northampton
Northamptonshire
NN7 2JN
Tel: 01604 862268
Email: bex@theoldcrownashton.co.uk
www.theoldcrownashton.co.uk

FOODIE
Reader Comment

"Lovely food, well presented, would highly recommend."
C.B.

The small village of Ashton is just a stones throw from the A508 midway between Northampton and Milton Keynes. Chef Ian and his wife Bex took over this lovely dining pub just a couple of years ago and have already made massive changes, which include new menus as well as good ales. Not surprising then that their reputation for good food is gradually spreading further afield.

The Old Crown is the heart of the village and is a warm and welcoming inn with a lovely safe garden to relax in the summer sunshine. Winter times the cosy interior is a great place to just sit back and watch the world go by.

As a chef and owner Ian ensures that all his produce is sourced locally wherever possible and meals prepared freshly in his kitchen. He sets high standards and expects his kitchen team to maintain them. You can expect a good choice from the menu, starters such as Fresh Crab with Gazpacho and Cucumber Sauce, Deep Fried Squid with Aioli or Grilled Goats Cheese with a Pine Nut and Herb Crust. Main courses may include Twice Cooked Pigs Cheeks with Parsnip Mash, Red Wine and Smoky Bacon, Local Pork Sausages with Bubble and Squeak and Cider Gravy or Honey Roast Duck Breast with Dauphinoise Potato Gratin. If you have a sweet tooth the dessert menu will delight with some delicious traditional favourites. Front of house, wife Bex is there to welcome you and ensure your visit is a memorable one.

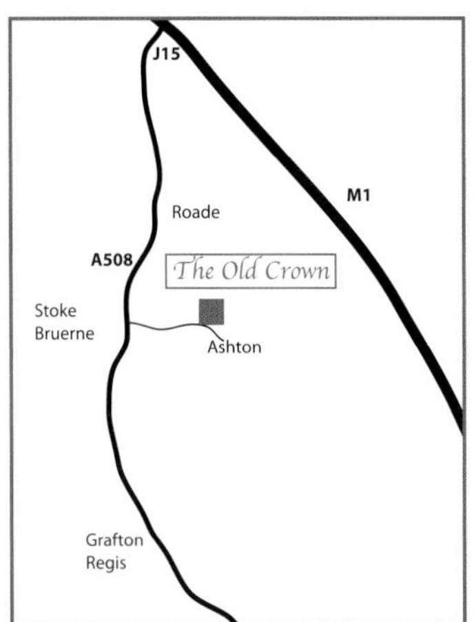

Opening Times:
Tue-Fri 12 noon to 3.00 pm & 6.00 pm - 11.30 pm
Sat 12 noon - 11.30 pm
Sun 12 noon - 10.30 pm

Food Served:
Tue-Fri 12 noon - 3.00 pm & 6.00 pm - 9.30 pm
Sat 12 noon - 9.30 pm
Sun 12 noon - 6.00 pm

Northampton Road
Grafton Regis
Northants NN12 7SR
Tel: 01908 542123
www.pubgraftonregis.com

Grafton Regis is a small village located on the main A508 midway between Milton Keynes and Northampton. This small friendly village with approximately 96 residents is home to The White Hart, a small 16th Century stone thatched property, owned by the Drake family for over 14 years.

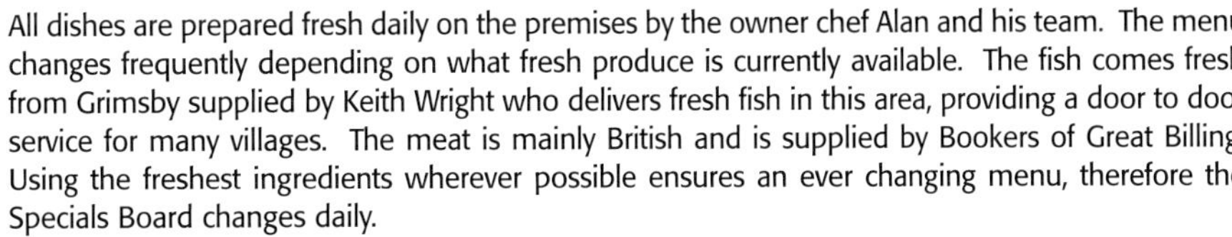

All dishes are prepared fresh daily on the premises by the owner chef Alan and his team. The menu changes frequently depending on what fresh produce is currently available. The fish comes fresh from Grimsby supplied by Keith Wright who delivers fresh fish in this area, providing a door to door service for many villages. The meat is mainly British and is supplied by Bookers of Great Billing. Using the freshest ingredients wherever possible ensures an ever changing menu, therefore the Specials Board changes daily.

Andy runs the front of house and says that they are constantly trying to improve on what they have, with the introduction of some new tables and chairs and a re-launch menu. They have changed the concept at the pub and now offer one big menu in all areas. There is a traditional lounge bar area, air conditioned restaurant and beautiful garden. Having this much commitment has it's rewards when they were awarded by Green King Brewery the title of "Catering Pub of the Year" winning first place from over 700 outlets.

The restaurant gets very busy, comfortably seating 26-29 covers, so you are stongly advised to book your table to avoid disappointment. You are also able to book the entire restaurant for functions providing the numbers are at least 24 up to a maximum of 29.

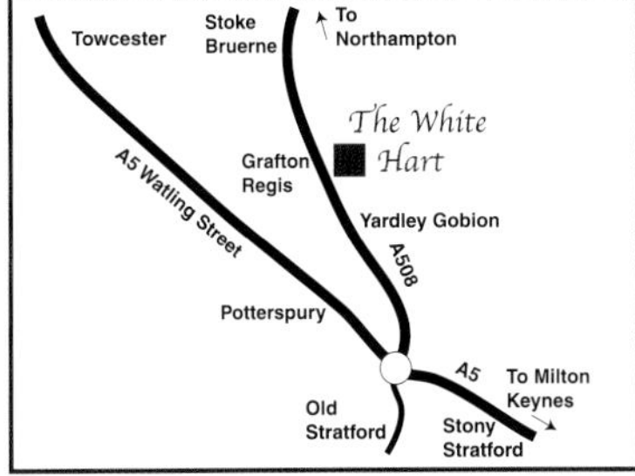

FOODIE
Reader Comment

"Excellent food, not too expensive and very friendly atmosphere."

J.I.

Food service times:
Mon Closed
Tue-Sat 12 noon - 2.00 pm & 6.00 pm - 9.30 pm
Sun 12 noon - 2.00 pm & 7.00 pm - 9.00 pm

Vouchers accepted Tue-Thurs only

Bar Restaurant

ALL WINNERS !!!

This year you have voted these restaurants your favourites throughout the four counties, thank you to everyone who voted and well done to Karen Byford from Milton Keynes who had her name drawn as the winner of our 2010 prize draw. She will be treated to a meal for two at Olivier's.

fine foods & wines

Stony Wine Emporium

2 Odell's Yard
Stony Stratford
Milton Keynes
Buckinghamshire
MK11 1AQ
Tel: 01908 267373
Email: info@stonywineemporium.co.uk
www.stonywineemporium.co.uk

The Stony Wine Emporium opened in October 2009 and is the creation of Simon & Caroline Stagnell. Simon has enjoyed over 20 years in the wine trade, representing a vast range of wineries, estates & icon producers. His passion, knowledge & experience gained over these years provided the inspiration to open a new wine shop concept situated in the charming historic market town of Stony Stratford in north Buckinghamshire.

All the wines have been tasted, carefully selected and represent the best available from their domaine. There are always over 250 wines available on the shelves, which are constantly changing as they discover new and exciting vineyards and producers.

They offer wine purchasing at all levels, from everyday drinking to premium estate wines. There is always an opportunity to taste when you visit along with access to good advice and guidance.

Private Tastings can be arranged for groups of friends, work colleagues and corporate clients, either at the shop or your choice of local venue, there are a large range of subjects on offer, which are aimed to be informative and fun.

The Wine Café is open daily serving lunches from 12.00 onwards offering some delicious anti pasti, cheese & meat platters to share, along with some tasty salads and light lunches. Dining is casual with a good selection of wines available by the glass and all the wines can be picked off the shelf for just a £5 supplement.

Opening times:
Mon Closed
Tue-Wed 10.00 am - 6.00 pm
Thur-Fri 10.00 am - 9.00 pm
Sat 9.00 am - 6.00 pm
Sun Closed

FLITTON HILL ORGANIC FARM SHOP

SOIL ASSOCIATION ORGANIC

Flitton Hill
Flitton
Bedfordshire MK45 2BE
Tel: 01525 860277
Mobile: 07885 625745
Email: farmercatlin@tiscali.co.uk
www.flittonhill.co.uk

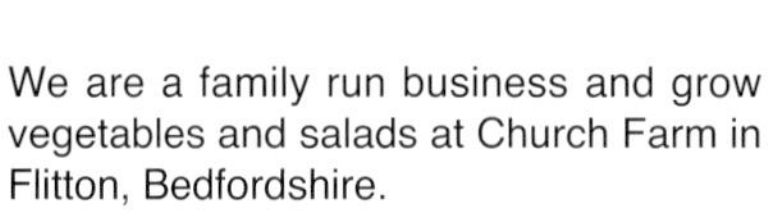

We are a family run business and grow vegetables and salads at Church Farm in Flitton, Bedfordshire.

Church Farm has a history of vegetable production going back over 70 years.

By the mid 1990's we had become very disillusioned with conventional vegetable growing. Not only were we working harder and harder for ever smaller returns but we also found that we had to use more and more chemicals on the crops for what were sometimes purely cosmetic reasons, e.g. to improve the skin finish on potatoes or the appearance of the leaves on leeks.

In 1997 the decision was taken to convert the farm to organic production and the farm was registered with the Soil Association gaining full organic status in 2000 after a three year conversion period.

At first we only supplied a large vegetable box scheme in London, and they took all of our produce and supported us during our first years as organic growers. We then began to supply other box schemes and in the autumn of 2005 The Farm Shop was opened which has proved to be a great success.

The farm grows a variety of crops including an acre of asparagus which is a big seller when it appears in the shop in April, for its short season.

We are committed to improving the environment on and around the farm and as well as restoring and planting many hedge rows and trees we are part of the Countryside Stewardship Scheme and have set aside a large acreage on Flitton Moor allowing it to revert to natural grassland. This part of the farm is open to the public via a circular pathway.

Opening times:
Thur 10.00 am - 5.00 pm
Fri 9.00 am - 6.00 pm
Sat 9.00 am - 4.00 pm

FRANKLINS
of thorncote
(Est. 25 years)

Trumpetons Farm
Thorncote Green
Sandy
Bedfordshire
SG19 1PU
T: 01767 627644 / 07771 927547
E: sales@franklinsfarm.co.uk
W: www.franklinsfarm.co.uk

"Free Range quality Poultry and Meat that is reared on the family Farm"

We are a traditional farm shop and butchery who specialise in rearing poultry as well as rearing our own cattle and lamb. We deal in locally shot game which includes partridge, pheasant, wild duck, venison, hare and rabbit. Some of our meat products are sourced from local farmers in our bid to reduce food miles.

We believe in providing the highest quality of poultry and meat products to our customers and strongly believe that we do this by providing our animals with the best welfare standards. Our customers tell us that they love shopping with Franklins because we are a REAL Farm Shop and our produce is of the highest quality and the best part of the experience is knowing the meat is reared on OUR farm.

Our farm shop is actually located on the Family Farm so our customers can see the animals grazing in the fields. Franklins are fortunate enough to have a butcher with over 40 years of experience who produces cuts that you just don't see in your modern day butchers. As well as the farm shop Franklins trade at local Farmers Markets and on the internet where we offer a courier service. Our produce can also be found at other local Farm shops and butchers particularly at Christmas, we also supply some local restaurants. **Order your Christmas produce from us, you will not be disappointed.**

"A REAL FARM SHOP not just a shop in the countryside"

Opening times:

Tue-Thur 9:00 – 17:00
Fri 9:00 – 18:00
Sat 9:00 – 15:00

The *Inspired Gourmet*

Cookery School

Milton Keynes

The Old Granary
Brooklands Farm
Broughton
Buckinghamshire MK16 0HU
Tel: 01908 692918
Email: info@inspiredgourmet.co.uk
www.inspiredgourmet.co.uk

Inspired Gourmet Cookery School in Milton Keynes offers inspiring and practical cookery courses and events for all ages and groups.

Develop fresh ideas. Learn new flavours and techniques.

The aim of our **cookery courses** is to inspire creativity in the kitchen – your kitchen. Our hand-on courses are friendly and professional, instilling you with confidence, offering you the tuition to develop your skills. Gift vouchers are available for all courses.

Cookery Courses • Cookery Parties • Catering • Corporate Events

Our **cookery parties**, suitable for all ages, are a unique way to celebrate any event.

We provide **catering** to the local area – to guarantee freshness and exclusivity of the dishes we create. We offer professional service and inspirational dishes, whether canapés, buffets or sit-down gourmet lunches and dinners.

Corporate Cookery is a perfect team-building event and we provide meeting facilities for you to round out your "away day".

Please stop by any time to see the facilities and organise your next party or event.

"More importantly can I say that we had a wonderful time on Friday and all thoroughly enjoyed the day, it was great fun and we can't thank you and Adam enough for our event." D. Lawson

"I learned so much about food, cooking, cooking techniques, flavours and all thoroughly enjoyable. John has an infectious love of food and cooking." F. Bernstein

"I just wanted to let you know we had a great day yesterday. Everyone is positively buzzing today. The team have all said today what a fantastic time they had and want to do it again." S. Knell, Sensient Flavors

"Many, many thanks for a superbly catered day on Saturday. Everyone thoroughly enjoyed all the lunch and the evening food, and has made many comments about the quality of the food and the friendliness of your staff. You really did make the day very easy for us." K. McIntosh

"I had to write straight away to say thank you both to yourself and Dave for such a fantastic evening. The menu was spot on, Dave was excellent, the venue perfect and it was really good value for money. We will certainly be trying out the dishes we made again. We will be recommending you to all of our friends and hopefully be back on another course ourselves." K. Davies

Food service times:
Mon-Sun 9.00 am - 11.00 pm

Unit 5, Station Court, Top Station Road, Brackley, Northamptonshire NN13 7UG
Tel: 01280 700016 Fax: 01280 700168
Email: food@mashandco.com www.mashandco.com

James and Kate Moulson are the couple behind Mash & Co Catering. Mash & Co produce quality food exquisitely presented, using the best available ingredients. This is all produced from their own commercial kitchen in Brackley, Northamptonshire.

James Moulson, head chef and director has had a varied career. He has worked at Claridges and also aboard the QEII and has also developed innovative products for well known high street retailers. He is also the face of 'Creative Cooks' which is a new project to come from the well known brand 'Epicure'. James has created some fantastic dishes in the Creative Cooks range.

Mash & Co can provide fantastic food for Weddings, Parties, Summer Balls or sumptuous buffets. They ensure that their attention to detail is constantly maintained, therefore providing a highly professional service from the excellent food through to their discreet and attentive staff.

Whether you are a real foodie or maybe you could use a helping hand with food ideas, Mash & Co can provide you with your ideal menu. Each menu can be tailor made just for you and served to your specifications. There is also the opportunity to taste their wonderful food before you choose them as your caterer.

Mash & Co is very much a friendly catering company. The company was created to provide a really personal feel and to ensure that the main priority for Mash & Co and its customers is quality.

THE GATEWAY TO REAL VILLAGE SHOPPING

BATTLERS GREEN FARM

RURAL SHOPPING VILLAGE & TEAROOMS

TAKE A BREAK & PAY A LEISURELY VISIT TO HERTFORDSHIRE'S UNIQUE BATTLERS GREEN FARM

In this lovely farmyard setting you'll find over a dozen traditional stores including the long-established **Battlers Green Farm Shop** with its superb range of high quality food and wines, as well as other prestigious retailers including **Aga** and **Fired Earth** showrooms, a fishmongers, a butchers, a pet shop, a craft studio and a holistic shop to name but a few. While you're here be sure to take a relaxing break in our spacious and distinctive tearooms, **The Bull Pen**. There's ample free parking so why not make a day of it?

BATTLERS GREEN FARM • COMMON LANE • RADLETT • HERTFORDSHIRE • WD7 8PH

TELEPHONE: 01923 856551 • WWW.BATTLERSGREENFARM.CO.UK

Just half a mile off the B462 (Radlett/Watford Road) take the New Road turning at the mini roundabout and we are half a mile on the right hand side.

BATTLERS GREEN FARM SHOP THE LOOSE BOX SUZANNE CONSTANTINE SHOES THE FLOWER GROVE DESTINY MAINE SAIL REITHS FURNITURE ANDREW BROWN HOME BRIMARK BUTCHERS CLASSIC FRAMING THE AGA SHOP FIRED EARTH THE BULL PEN TEA ROOMS DANCING HENS CRAFT STUDIO

Taste Real Food Bedford is an ambitious venture incorporating taste education through *Look, Touch, Taste and Feel.*

how will joining benefit you?

joining a forum of likeminded people
developing an interest in food sourcing and preparation
providing a 'fun' way for raising funds to support a local community project highlighting the Taste of Real Food
helping to bring approved local producers and outlets into the minds of local people

uniting the community in the Taste of Real Food

The Taste Real Food Bedford Project 2010 is supported by our Taste Real Food members and funded by The Bedfordshire and Luton Community Foundation's Grassroots Grant Fund

If you would like to find out more contact:
Sue Miller, Taste Real Food Bedford Leader and Taste Real Food UK Director.
Email, tasterealfoodbedford@ntlworld.com, Telephone 07753 780607

TASTE REAL FOOD UK
Stone House, Corve Street, Ludlow, Shropshire SY8 1DG *Tel:* 01584 875119 *E-mail:* info@tasterealfood.com *Web:* www.tasterealfood.com
TASTE REAL FOOD Bedford
10, Irwin Road, Bedford, MK40 3UL *Tel:* 07753 780607 *E-mail:* tasterealfoodbedford@ntlworld.com

PRIESTLEY FARM SHOP

Church Road
off Temple Way
Flitwick
Beds MK45 5AN
Tel: 01525 712397
www.priestleyfarm.co.uk

For over fifty years Priestley Farm has been a family run business growing vegetables, potatoes and salads. The farm shop was established in 1982 and over the years has grown in size to accommodate a variety of home grown produce. Our fields are kept in top condition with the use of organic manures, we sow our own seeds and grow them in greenhouses until they are ready for planting. Our irrigation system ensures that crops are well watered to produce a wide variety of high quality fresh vegetables for sale in our farm shop throughout the year.

Our range of products include: local fresh meat, sausages, bacon and meat pies. Milk, Jersey cream, Jersey butter, fresh free range eggs from our own chickens and when in season both duck and goose eggs. Homemade cakes, pies, tarts, bread, rolls, teacakes a fine selection of jams, marmalades, fruit juices and honey produced from bees on the farm.

We have a children's play area and pet's corner to ensure the kids are kept entertained!

Because we are a working farm please note that we are only open to the public Thursday, Friday and Saturday.

We look forward to welcoming you soon!

Opening times:
Thur-Sat 9.30am - 5.00 pm

Cople Road
Cardington
Bedfordshire
MK44 3SH
Tel: 01234 831222
Email: sales@summerhillfarmshop.co.uk
www.summerhillfarmshop.co.uk

Set in the picturesque village of Cardington, home of the famous Cardington airship hangars, the Summerhill Farm Shop has an outstanding reputation.

Thanks to Andy's family heritage of butchering, we excel in providing top quality meat. We are proud to produce our own homemade items, including sausages (one of which is our exclusive 'Hangar Banger') and burgers. We locally raise our own British White Beef on the Southill Estate. The herds are entirely grass-fed. Whether it's lamb, pork, free range poultry, game or exotic's – we take great care in butchering the finest cuts of chosen meats for you. From BBQ's in the summer to turkeys at Christmas, we always provide the very best for every occasion.

Our appreciation of good healthy food is enhanced by using our local suppliers. Fresh eggs and chickens arrive to us from a neighbouring farm. Local milk, cream and dairy products are delivered direct to our barn doors daily. Our fruit and vegetables arrive fresh and crisp, changing regularly with the seasons.

Our delicatessen has a fantastic range of cheeses and fresh cold meats complementing our range of breads and biscuits. We supply the best sauces to go with the best food. Whether it's a traditional roast dinner, a hot and spicy barbecue or a really great sandwich, we have sauces, olives, honeys and seasoning to add to any meal.

We offer a wonderful selection of cakes. Gooey chocolate cake, sticky battenburg, or a refreshing orange and lemon sponge cake, these are just some of the delights on offer.

Summerhill Farm Shop provides the finest of British wines that have consistently won awards for their quality and flavour. Warden Abbey, Bedfordshire's only working vineyard, is located a short distance from the shop. We also love our range of country fruit wines. It's not just about wine however, we provide selected traditional ciders, ales and spirits.

A gorgeous converted barn, we are 3 miles to the east of Bedford with plenty of parking spaces. The Summerhill Farm Shop is an idyllic, stress free place to come and visit.

Opening times:
Tues-Fri 7.30 am - 6.00 pm
Sat 7.30 am - 5.00 pm
Sun 10.00 am - 4.00 pm

Black's
EVENTS

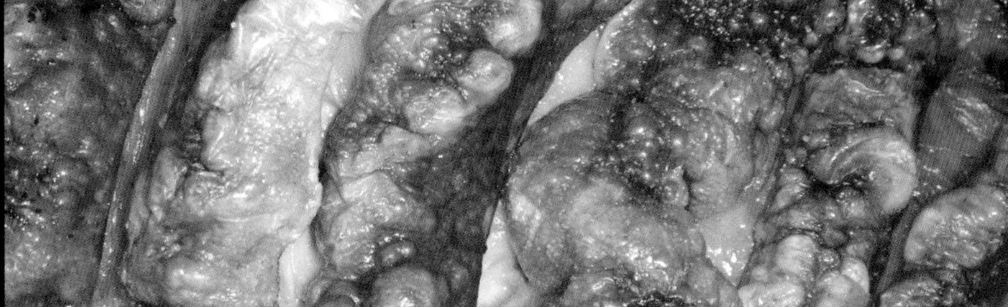

A Versatile and Fresh Catering Company

Ideal for Corporate Events, Weddings, Private Parties, Product Launches, Christenings.....

Specialists in traditionally spit-roasted meats and barbeques accompanied by homemade canapé's, side dishes and delicious desserts.

Moroccan themed events, our giant tagines will make it a night to remember.

We can tailor our menus to suit your needs providing as much or as little as you require.

Our team of staff are professional and smart and we pride ourselves on providing excellent service and mouthwatering food that you will want to taste again and again.

Our website has sample menus to tease your taste buds.

www.blacksevents.com
Email: mark@blacksevents.com
Tel: 01327 352962 Mob: 07773 422074

Best Butchers Ltd

Unit 5
Lower Rectory Farm
Great Brickhill
Milton Keynes
MK17 9AF
Tel: 01908 375275
Email: bestbutchers@btconnect.com
www.thebestbutchers.co.uk

Quality, variety and a commitment to personal service sum up Simon Boddy's "Best Butchers Ltd".

This absolutely spotless shop was opened in 1994 on a working organic farm and specialises in supplying locally sourced meat. Besides joints and cuts of beef, lamb, pork and poultry the shop is renowned for its fine pork, beef and lamb sausages all prepared on the premises along with bacon, dry-cured and slowly smoked over beech. Air-dried then smoked, Brickhill ham is Simon's own adaption of Parma ham and to complement this, a fine selection of English and Continental cheeses. Fish lovers will be pleased to learn that on Fridays and Saturdays, Simon along with Liz Fryer, source direct from Billingsgate market all the fresh fish and then expertly prepare it for you to enjoy.

Acclaimed by Rose Prince of the Daily Telegraph that the air-dried coppa was the best air-dried meat she had tasted in Britain and also rated in the Sunday Observer as "Best Deli".

Opening times:
Mon-Fri 8.00 am - 5.00 pm **Sat** 8.00 am - 2.00 pm

Love Food. Love Frosts.

At Frosts we believe in providing good quality, affordable fresh food, for good living. We source only the finest ingredients and hand select all of our products to compliment seasonal changes.

We stock an extensive range of products including locally sourced fresh fruit and vegetables, hand made cakes and pies and a wide range of packaged produce from baked beans and cereals to artisan chutneys. Our fully stocked delicatessen counter offers delicious cheeses, pâtés and olives which taste fantastic alongside our bread which is baked freshly every morning. Whether you are looking for that extra treat for a dinner party or simply need a pint of milk, Frosts Food Hall offers great value convenience shopping.

Open seven days a week we have created a shopping experience that will meet all of your culinary requirements.

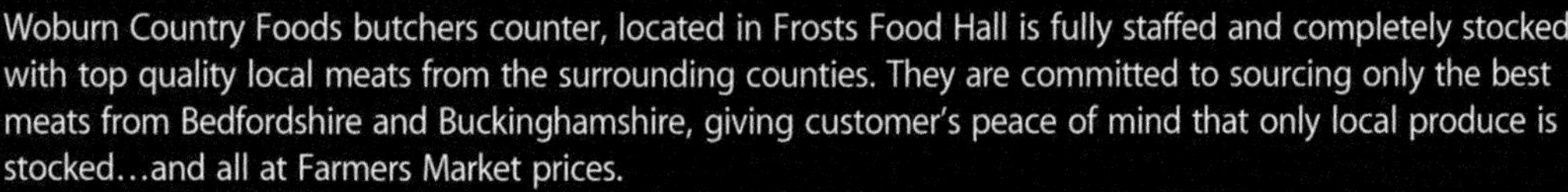

Woburn Country Foods butchers counter, located in Frosts Food Hall is fully staffed and completely stocked with top quality local meats from the surrounding counties. They are committed to sourcing only the best meats from Bedfordshire and Buckinghamshire, giving customer's peace of mind that only local produce is stocked...and all at Farmers Market prices.

Frosts Garden Centre at Woburn Sands, Newport Road, Woburn Sands, Milton Keynes, MK17 8UE **Tel:** 01908 583511

www.frostsgroup.com

Everyone deserves quality food

Café, Towcester.

Why not visit your nearest Waitrose and share in its passion for food and reputation for excellent customer service. Its offer of quality products, honestly priced within a spacious environment makes food shopping a pleasure. Many of our stores now have a café for you to enjoy.

No matter what your taste, cooking talents or time constraints, there's something for everyone. With dedicated food counters - delicatessen, patisseries, cheese, fish and meat - boasting only the highest quality foods, there's a huge choice to be had.

With Cheese, Fish and Meat Specialists at the counters, you can ensure you'll get not only the best selection of produce to choose from, but also the finest advice - whether that be for everyday eating or party planning.

Manor Road
Brackley
Northants NN13 6BE
01280 703333

Meadow Walk
High Street
Buckingham
Bucks MK18 1RS
01280 813479

13 Bowen Square
Daventry
Northants NN11 4DR
01327 705939

3 Leyton Road
Harpenden
Herts AL5 2TJ
01582 765161

The Lairage
Bedford Road
Hitchin
Herts SG5 2UG
01462 423399

9 Waterborne Walk
Leighton Buzzard
Beds LU7 1DH
01525 378334

728 Midsummer Boulevard
Central Milton Keynes
Bucks MK9 3NJ
01908 672677

1 Ermine Close
Mayne Avenue
St Albans
Herts AL3 4JZ
01727 831117

Richmond Road
Towcester
Northants NN12 6HZ
01327 354994

Waitrose

Having won a whole host of medals and trophies for their wines, there's something for every taste, every meal and all occasions at Waitrose.

As healthy eating is such a hot topic at the moment, it's great to have a range of foods, such as Waitrose Wholesome, that are both easy to choose - and use - on a daily basis. Containing 140 simple, inherently nutritious foods including nuts, seeds, cereals, grains, dried fruits, beans and pulses, the range is ideal for both food lovers and the health conscious alike.

And with a range of excellent services available such as Waitrose Entertaining, Waitrose Deliver and Quick Check, there's more to Waitrose than meets the eye. For more information on these services, visit www.waitrose.com

Aubergine Fine Foods

73 High Street
Woburn Sands
Bucks
MK17 8QY
Tel: 01908 582020
Email: auberginedeli@btconnect.com

Aubergine Fine Foods is an independent, family-owned delicatessen in Woburn Sands, established by local residents Jill and John Goulding. Run by food lovers for food lovers, Aubergine strives to offer international speciality foods alongside the finest locally-sourced produce.

The ever expanding range includes British and continental cheeses, salamis and chorizos, pastas, cooking sauces, preserves, chocolates, breads and biscuits, plus all the kitchen cupboard essentials. Fresh fish is available to order direct from Billingsgate Market three times a week.

Wherever possible Aubergine sources foods from local, small-scale producers, including free-range eggs from Cranfield; bacon, sausages and hams from their butcher's own farm in Bedfordshire; bread from Ampthill; organic milk from Flitwick; plus honey, vegetables and delicious home-made cakes from Woburn Sands itself.

In addition, there is an increasing range of 'free from' foods for people with special dietary requirements, including gluten-free pastas, cereals and biscuits. Aubergine is also an ethical and environmentally responsible business. Many products are fairly traded, offering producers in the developing world a better deal, and all the shop's own packaging is bio-degradable, recyclable, or from a sustainable source.

Latest developments include a new lunch menu offering pasta dishes, home-made savoury tartlets, filled ciabatta rolls and gourmet salads, plus great coffee and fresh fruit smoothies. A business and event menu is also available with free local delivery. And for those of you looking for something a bit different for your special event or even wedding, we can provide a portable wood fired pizza oven with your personal pizza chef.

Whatever your culinary tastes, if you're passionate about food and looking for an alternative to the supermarket experience, pay a visit to Aubergine - your local, independent fine food store.

Opening times:
Mon-Thur 8.00 am - 5.00 pm
Fri 8.00 a[illegible]0 pm
Sat 9.00[illegible]0 pm

Riverford organic veg

+ lots more to your door

stock up your kitchen + cut down on shopping trips

Riverford delivers award-winning organic food fresh from Sacrewell Farm straight to your door. There's nothing Riverford doesn't know about fruit and veg (they've been growing it for nearly 25 years) but the farm has plenty more to offer. Choose from a range of weekly organic essentials like eggs, milk, meat, juice and cereal, and even wine, chocolate, pasta and olive oil. Delivery is free and you don't need to be at home.

get inspired + cook seasonally

You'll want to make the most of all that fresh seasonal food and Riverford makes it easy. With each delivery your local vegman (or lady) will bring up to eight new recipes to inspire you to feed your family better. Forget boring boiled vegetables: swap them for sweet and tasty honey-glazed carrots or grilled courgettes and tomatoes with basil dressing. Riverford's website is bursting with even more recipes. And if you ever run out of ideas, just call the team at the farm for help.

easy to order

Ordering is easy and flexible. Riverford delivers weekly, fortnightly or whenever suits and you can stop and start deliveries as often as you like. Make up your own order from the full range or try a vegbox from just £8.95 with free delivery.

www.riverford.co.uk/sacrewell

0845 078 6868

Delicatessen Estrella

2A High Street
Winslow
Buckinghamshire
MK18 3HF
Tel: 01296 712466
www.delicatessenestrella.co.uk

Located in the heart of the pretty market town in Winslow, right opposite the Market Square, Delicatessen Estrella specialises in providing the best food and ingredients available to bring you the flavours of the Mediterranean. Helen and John Knight have a passion for all food, especially that of Spain and North Africa and always stock an excellent range of unusual Spanish products, including charcuterie and cheeses.

Throughout the shop the emphasis is always on food of the highest quality, which they source from the best suppliers in their fields, including cheeses from Neal's Yard Dairy and Spanish meats from Brindisa. Helen's home baking is a huge hit with customers. From pasties, pies and quiches to cupcakes, biscuits and cakes. You will also find a range of delicious fresh salads and seasonal soups to take home. An excellent range of ethically produced coffees are ground to order and fresh artisan bread is available several days a week.

Estrella opens every Friday night until 7pm to make it easy for busy workers to pick up a one stop meal. This might range from a tapas selection or an antipasto plate to a cheese board, cake or pudding. Complement your food with their selection of great wines and sherries, or try a few bottles from their popular range of locally brewed real ales.

So if you love good food and are looking for the best products and ingredients for yourself, or a food or drink related gift like their popular Christmas baskets and hampers made to order, make sure you visit Delicatessen Estrella.

Opening times:

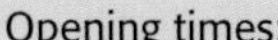

Mon-Thur 10:00 – 17:30
Fri 10:00 – 19:00
Sat 09:30 – 17:00
Sun Farmers Market Sundays (1st Sunday of each month) and December 10:00 – 14:00

Browns of Stagsden FARM SHOP

Manor Farm
High Street
Stagsden
Bedford
MK43 8SQ
Tel: 01234 822330
Email: info@brownsofstagsden.co.uk
www.brownsofstagsden.co.uk

The Brown family has farmed in and around Bedfordshire for many years, and three generations are now involved in the business. The family has always taken great pride in growing crops and rearing cattle, pigs and turkeys, so they decided to open a shop at Manor Farm, in the beautiful village of Stagsden.

The shop has been trading for five and a half years and has recently been renovated and expanded, allowing the Browns to offer a greater range of locally grown produce to an ever increasing customer base.

Traditional breeds of cattle, pigs and turkeys are reared for the shop using home-grown grain where possible, whilst lambs and free range chickens are reared locally.

Game is also available when in season. All sausages, burgers and ready meals are prepared on site and you will also be able to buy local vegetables, cheeses, hams, organic flour, fresh bread, gluten-free cakes, free range eggs, local milk, ice-creams and tempting accompaniments.

In the run up to Christmas - a very busy time of the year for Browns - you will be able to pre-order your home reared turkey and any other meats, or choose from our wide range of hampers which make for excellent presents.

So if you are looking for something different and enjoy good quality produce, please pay the shop a visit, where our helpful staff will offer you a warm welcome. Why not stop and enjoy a coffee whilst you shop with us?

Opening times:
Tue-Thur 9.00 am - 5.00 pm
Fri 9.00 am - 6.00 pm (Fresh Fish available 9.00 am - 3.00 pm)
Sat 9.00 am - 4.00 pm

the larder

The Old Farmyard
Castle Ashby
Northamptonshire
NN7 1LF
Tel: 01604 696742
Email: info@thelarderuk.co.uk
www.thelarderuk.co.uk

The Larder Delicatessen is set in an idyllic location, at the rural shopping yard in the picturesque village of Castle Ashby, the ancestral home of the 7th Marquis of Northampton. Just 8 miles from Northampton and less than a 30 minute drive from Milton Keynes.

Owned by husband and wife team Neil and Katie. Neil brings a vast amount of experience as an award winning chef, complemented by Katie who ensures that a warm friendly service always awaits you.

The Larder Deli

The Larder Deli offers a wonderful culinary shopping experience. Specialising in quality fine foods, including a wide selection of artisan cheeses, local farm produce, top quality hams, patés, pies, and quiches. Locally brewed beers, fine wines, liqueurs and spirits. Our shelves are packed with a mouth watering variety of pickles, preserves, oils, cooks ingredients and those hard to find foods.

Why not take advantage of our pre-ordering service for all your entertaining needs. We are able to produce a range of dishes from canapés, starters, soups, main courses and salads. Our range of fine patiserie desserts are also ideal when entertaining. Or maybe choose one of our pre-selected cheeseboards, alternatively we can prepare to your individual tastes.

Castle Ashby is the perfect location for a picnic, whether visiting the gardens or a spot of fishing by the lakes. So why not choose one of our recyclable picnic boxes, available in three sizes, these can be pre-ordered or prepared for you on the day.

Our hampers make the perfect gift for any occasion. Choose from our specially designed range or hand pick your own. Both local and national delivery service available.

The Larder Catering

Whether you're planning a corporate or private function Neil can manage your requirements, from initial expert advice and planning to delivery of exceptional food, with 'wow factor' presentation, on time and to your budget. The Larder caters for events of all sizes including: family and social celebrations, picnics, dinner parties and corporate events.

Opening times:
Tue-Sat 10.00 am - 5.00 pm
Sundays and Bank Holidays 11.00 am - 5.00 pm

Glebe Road
Mears Ashby
Northants
NN6 0DL
Tel: 01604 812371
Email: enquiries@beckworthemporium.co.uk
www.beckworthemporium.co.uk

Beckworth Emporium is a contemporary plant centre housing a Food Hall, Produce Market, Garden Nursery and Restaurant which, since its opening in April 2009, has attracted thousands of visitors who have branded it a "truly unique shopping experience."

The Food Hall and Deli is home to Hambleton Farms – a family-run traditional farmers, butchers and game dealers supplying high-quality traditional fresh meat, game, home-made pork pies and speciality pies, home-cooked meats, hand-made sausages, haslets and much more.

A large range of high-quality ready meals and shortcrust pastry pies are also available alongside a wide selection of international, national and local cheese.

Fresh bread is baked daily on site and on Wednesdays fish lovers will delight in fresh catches from our Grimsby fishmonger.

We've divided our Restaurant into three atmospheric areas, each individually designed including table-service offering a wide choice of delicious wholesome food using Beckworth ingredients. The stunning garden atrium is ideal for enjoying coffee, lunch and afternoon teas surrounded by our favourite colourful plants, or if the sun is shining, visitors can sit outside in the garden terrace.

The Produce Market provides an endless selection of delicious fruit and vegetables, some of which are grown on site. This fabulous display is sold alongside a range of groceries, flowers and plants.

Opening times:
Mon-Sat 8.00 am - 6.00 pm
Sun 11.00 am - 5.00 pm
Restaurant:
Mon-Sat 8.00 am - 5.00 pm
Sun 9.00 am - 5.00 pm

We work hard for you to select the best of seasonal produce – offering real taste and value for money. As you pass through, you will find a selection of grocery stalls – teas and coffees, pastas and rices, cakes and biscuits, crisps and snacks and even beers and wines.

We pride ourselves on offering top-quality local produce, when possible, from suppliers who have a focus on great taste and a passion for good food.

Wander into our Garden Nursery and you'll discover a stunning array of colourful, seasonal plants, garden essentials and our container collection.

The majority of plants available are grown in our nursery enabling us to offer an adventurous range of top-quality bedding plants at very competitive prices.

These plants can be used to create a fantastic selection of beautiful hanging baskets and planted containers, brilliant for brightening up any patio and they make wonderful gifts. And if you're a novice, our expert grower Peter Taylor and the team are on hand to offer specialist tips and advice.

We look forward to welcoming you to Beckworth Emporium soon.

the FOOD BARN

good food ...naturally

Baldock Lane
Willian
Hertfordshire
SG6 2AE
Tel: 01462 685363
Email: info@foodbarnwillian.co.uk

At The Food Barn, in the picturesque village of Willian, Hertfordshire, we have a passion for bringing you the best of quality British food.

We provide the freshest seasonal foods, dealing with local producers to support farmers and growers while providing your kitchen with the very best the British countryside has to offer.

- **Fresh fish and shellfish from Norfolk and Cornwall...**
- **Quality free range meat from the farm next door...**
- **Outdoor reared chicken...**
- **Traditional, handmade British farmhouse cheese...**
- **Local fruit and vegetables...**
- **Fine wines, and over 20 quality local ciders and beers...**
- **Much more besides..!**

Opening times:
Tue-Fri 10.00 am - 6.00 pm **Sat** 9.00 am - 5.00 pm

Smiths Farm Shop

Smith's Farm Shop in Northamptonshire is a retailer of quality fresh farm foods and fine country produce. Selling fresh seasonal fruit and vegetables from British growers, including produce grown on their own farm behind the shop at Chapel Brampton. Aiming to source from producers most local ensures products arrive on the shelves in near-perfect condition, bursting with flavour and with the highest nutritional value. Regular customers say they come back time and again because Smith's produce can't be beaten for freshness and flavour, all at prices that compare well against larger U.K. food retailers.

Outside the Chapel Brampton shop you will find garden and pet supplies, plants and solid fuels. Inside the shop you will be greeted by a spacious layout for all the main food categories such as fruit and vegetables, jams and preserves, frozen foods, delicatessen, dairy products, eggs, cakes and pastries, bakery and meat. The quiet, relaxed atmosphere will help make your shopping trip more of a pleasurable experience, and less of a chore. They also stock ranges of non-food products, mainly for the home, garden and pets along with a small selection of greeting cards.

A great shopping experience awaits you at Smith's Farm Shop. For your convenience, they have a large car park right outside the shop entrance. Friendly members of staff are always ready to help carry your purchases to the car. They provide a relaxed and enjoyable shopping experience and at the Chapel Brampton site, you will find several other attractions to add a bit of fun and interest to your shopping trip!

Chapel Brampton Shop
Tel: 01604 843206
Brampton Lane, Chapel Brampton, Northampton, Northamptonshire NN6 8AA
Mon-Sat 9.00am - 5.30pm Sun 10.00am - 1.00pm

Great Billing Shop
Tel: 01604 412111
Billing Garden Village, The Causeway, Great Billing, Northamptonshire NN3 9EX
Mon-Sun 10.00am - 4.30pm

FARMERS MARKETS

Whilst every effort has been made compiling this list, we cannot accept responsibility when dates/times/places are changed.

Bedfordshire

Ampthill	The Prince of Wales pub car park	Last Saturday every month (except December)	9.00am - 1.00pm
Bedford	Harpur Square	2nd & 4th Thursday every month	9.00am - 2.00pm
Biggleswade	Market Square	3rd Wednesday every month	9.00am - 2.00pm
Cranfield	The Cross Keys pub	2nd Sunday every month	9.00am - 1.00pm
Dunstable Downs	Chiltern Gateway Centre	1st Sunday every month (except January)	10.00am - 2.00pm
Leighton Buzzard	High Street	3rd Saturday every month	9.00am - 2.00pm
Milton Ernest	Garden Centre Country Food Fayre	3rd Saturday every month	10.00am - 3.00pm
Sandy	Sandy Car Park	1st Saturday every month (except January)	9.00am - 1.00pm
Shefford	High Street	2nd Saturday every month	9.00am - 1.00pm
Woburn	The Pitching's, Woburn	3rd Sunday every month	11.00am - 3.00pm

Buckinghamshire

Aylesbury	Old Market Square	4th Tuesday every month	9.00am - 2.00pm
Beaconsfield	Windsor End, The Old Town	4th Saturday every month	9.00am - 12.30pm
Buckingham	Old Cattle Pens, High Street	1st Tuesday every month	7.30am - 1.00pm
Little Chalfont	Village Hall car park, Cokes Lane	2nd Saturday every month	9.00am - 1.00pm
Marlow	Dean Street car park	Every Sunday	10.00am - 1.00pm
Newport Pagnell	Market Hill, High Street	3rd Friday every month	9.00am - 2.00pm
Olney	Market Place	1st Sunday every month	10.00am - 2.00pm
Prestwood	Hildreths Garden Centre, Wycombe Rd.	Every Friday	8.00am - 1.00pm
Princes Risborough	High Street	3rd Thursday every month	8.30am - 1.30pm
Stony Stratford	Market Square	Last Friday every month	8.30am - 1.30pm
Wendover	Off High Street	3rd Saturday every month	10.00am - 1.00pm
Winslow	Market Square	First Sunday every month	11.00am - 2.00pm
Wolverton	Market Halls car park, Town Hall	1st & 3rd Saturdays every month	9.00am - 1.00pm

Hertfordshire

Dane End	Dane End Memorial Hall	2nd Saturday every month	10.30am - 12.30pm
Great Amwell	Van Hage Garden Company	1st Thursday every month	9.00am - 1.00pm
Gt Hormead	Village Hall	1st Saturday every month	10.00am - 12.30pm
Harpenden	Lower High Street	4th Saturday every month	10.00am - 2.00pm
Hatfield	White Lion Square	1st Saturday every month (except January)	9.00am - 2.00pm
Hertford	Market Place	2nd Saturday every month	9.00am - 1.00pm
Hertford Heath	Village Hall	3rd Sunday every month	9.00am - 1.00pm
Hitchin	Riverside	Last Saturday every month	8.00am - 2.00pm
Hoddesdon	The Clock Tower	3rd Friday every month	9.00am - 2.00pm
Leominster	Corn Square	2nd Saturday every month	9.00am - 1.00pm
Little Hadham	Village Hall	Last Saturday every month	9.00am - 12.00 noon
Royston	Town Hall	1st Friday every month	9.30am - 1.00pm
Sandon	Village Hall	3rd Saturday every month	9.30am - 12 noon
St Albans	Town Hall	2nd Sunday every month	9.00am - 2.00pm
Tring	Market Place	Alternate Saturdays	9.00am - 12.15pm

Northamptonshire

Brackley	Market Place	3rd Saturday every month	9.00am - 1.00pm
Daventry	High Street	1st Saturday every month	8.30am - 1.30pm
Higham Ferrers	Market Square	Last Saturday every month	8.00am - 3.00pm
Kettering	Wicksteed Park	3rd Sunday every month	9.00am - 2.00pm
Northampton	Market Square	3rd Thursday every month	9.00am - 1.30pm
Oundle	Market Street	2nd Saturday every month	9.00am - 2.00pm
Towcester	Richmond Rd car park	2nd Friday every month	9.00am - 2.00pm
Wellingborough	Market Place	Last Thursday every month	9.00am - 2.00pm

more reader recommendations

more reader recommendations

65 

The Alford Arms

Frithsden
Nr Hemel Hempstead
Hertfordshire
HP1 3DD
Tel: 01442 864480
Email: info@alfordarmsfrithsden.co.uk
www.alfordarmsfrithsden.co.uk

---

66 **Amble Inn**
182 Station Road, Harpenden, Herts AL5 4UL
Tel: 01582 621824 **Email:** info@ambleinn.co.uk
www.ambleinn.co.uk

---

67 **Angelos**
Springwood Park, Grendon Underwood, Aylesbury, Bucks HP18 0TF
Tel: 01296 771155

---

68 **The Angel Restaurant**
47 Bicester Road, Long Crendon, Aylesbury, Bucks HP18 9EE
Tel: 01844 208268 Email: info@angelrestaurant.co.uk
www.angelrestaurant.co.uk

---

69 **The Barge Inn**
15 Newport Road, Woolstone, Milton Keynes MK15 0AE
Tel: 01908 233841
www.vintageinn.co.uk

---

70 **The Bell Hotel & Inn**
21 Bedford Street, Woburn, Beds MK17 9QB
Tel: 01525 290280
www.bellinn-woburn.co.uk

---

71 **The Bell Inn**
Main Street, Beachampton, Bucks MK19 6DX
Tel: 01908 563861 **Email:** info@thebellrestaurant.co.uk
www.thebellrestaurant.co.uk

---

72 

The Birch

20 Newport Road
Woburn
Buckinghamshire
MK17 9HX
Tel: 01525 290295
Email: info@birchwoburn.com
www.birchwoburn.com

---

73 **The Belvedere**
Ardmore House Hotel, 54 Lemsford Road, St Albans, Herts AL1 3PR
Tel: 01727 859313
www.ardmorehousehotel.co.uk

---

74 

The Black Horse

Ireland
Shefford
Bedfordshire
SG17 5QL
Tel: 01462 811398
Email: info@blackhorseireland.com
www.blackhorseireland.com

---

75 **The Boot at Sarratt**
The Green, Sarratt, Rickmansworth, Herts WD3 6BL
Tel: 01923 262247 **Email:** info@thebootsarratt.co.uk
www.thebootsarratt.co.uk

---

76 **The Brampton Halt**
Pitsford Road, Chapel Brampton, Northants NN6 8BA
Tel: 01604 842676 **Email:** bramptonhalt@mcmanuspub.co.uk
www.mcmanuspub.co.uk

---

77 **Brasserie Blanc**
Chelsea House, 301 Avebury Blvd, Central Milton Keynes, Bucks MK9 2GA
Tel: 01908 546590
www.brasserieblanc.com

78

The Brocket Arms

Ayot St. Lawrence
Welwyn
Hertfordshire
AL6 9BT
Tel: 01438 820250
Email: bookings@brocketarms.com
www.brocketarms.com

---

79 **The Bull**
Cottered, Buntingford, Nr Stevenage, Herts SG9 9QP
Tel: 01763 281243 **Email:** reservations@thehillside.co.uk
www.thehillside.co.uk

---

80 **The Chequers at Millbrook**
Millbrook, Beds MK45 2JB
Tel: 01525 403835

81 **The Chequers Inn**
Kiln Lane, Wooburn Common, Bucks HP10 0JQ
Tel: 01628 529575 **Email:** info@chequers-inn.com
www.chequers-inn.com

82 **Chez Jerome**
26 Church Street, Dunstable, Beds LU5 4RU
Tel: 01582 603310 **Email:** info@chezjerome.co.uk
www.chezjerome.co.uk

83 **The Crooked Chimney**
Cromer Hyde Lane, Lemsford, Welwyn Garden City, Herts AL8 7XE
Tel: 01707 397021
www.vintageinn.co.uk

84 **Durbar Restaurant**
156 Wellingborough Road, Northampton NN1 4DU
Tel: 01604 604650 **Email:** info@durbar.co.uk
www.durbar.co.uk

85 **Earls Restaurant**
119 Dunstable Street, Ampthill, Beds MK45 2NG
Tel: 01525 404024 **Email:** earlsrestaurant@tiscali.co.uk
www.earlsofampthill.com

86 **The Falcon**
Riverside English Bistro, Rushden Road, Bletsoe, Beds MK44 1QN
Tel: 01234 781222 **Email:** thefalcona6@aol.com
www.thefalconbletsoe.co.uk

87 **Fawsley Hall**
Fawsley, Northants NN11 3BA
Tel: 01327 892000 **Email:** info@fawsleyhall.com
www.fawsleyhall.com

88 **The Five Arrows Hotel**
High Street, Waddesdon, Aylesbury, Bucks HP18 0JE
Tel: 01296 651727 **Email:** five.arrows@nationaltrust.org.uk
www.waddesdon.org.uk/five_arrows

89 **The Five Bells**
1 Northill Road, Cople, Beds MK44 3TU
Tel: 01234 838289 **Email:** kilroy@fivebellscople.co.uk
www.fivebellscople.co.uk

90 **The Fox and Hounds**
Harlestone Road, Lower Harlestone, Northants NN7 4EW
Tel: 01604 821251
www.thefoxandhoundsharlestone.co.uk

91 

Flamed Foods
Barbeque Event Catering
Tel: 01908 691010
Email: info@flamedfoods.co.uk
www.flamedfoods.co.uk

92 **The Fox at Willian**
Willian, Herts SG6 2AE
Tel: 01462 480233 **Email:** reservations@foxatwillian.co.uk
www.foxatwillian.co.uk

93 **The George & Dragon**
Watton-at-Stone, Herts SG14 3TA
Tel: 01920 830285 **Email:** pub@georgeanddragon.co.uk
www.georgeanddragonwatton.co.uk

94 **The Grand Union**
The Three Locks, Leighton Road, Stoke Hammond, Bucks MK17 9DD
Tel: 01525 270214 **Email:** info@gugroup.co.uk
www.gugroup.co.uk/threelocks

95 **The Grange**
132 Dunthorne Way, Grange Farm, Milton Keynes, Bucks MK8 0LW
Tel: 01908 340607
www.thegrangemk.co.uk

96 **Grove Lock**
Grove, Leighton Buzzard, Beds LU7 0QU
Tel: 01525 380940 **Email:** grovelock@fullers.co.uk

97 **The Hare and Hounds**
The Village, Old Warden, Beds SG18 9HQ
Tel: 01767 627225
www.hareandhoundsoldwarden.co.uk

98 **Hartwell House & Spa**
Oxford Road, Nr Aylesbury, Bucks HP17 8NR
Tel: 01296 747444 **Email:** info@hartwell-house.com
www.hartwell-house.com

99 **The Hillside Restaurant & Patisserie**
54 High Street, Wheathampstead, Herts AL4 8AR
Tel: 01582 833111 **Email:** reservations@thehillside.co.uk
www.thehillside.co.uk

100 **The Hopping Hare**
18 Hopping Hill Gardens, Duston, Northants NN5 6PF
Tel: 01604 580090 **Email:** info@hoppinghare.com
www.hoppinghare.com

101 **Hunters Restaurant**
The Olde Red Lion, High Street, Kislingbury, Northants NN7 4AQ
Tel: 01604 830219 **Email:** enquiries@theolderedlion.net
www.theolderedlion.net

102 **Jacoby's Bar & Restaurant**
Churchgate House, 15 West Street, Ware, Herts SG12 9EE
Tel: 01920 469181 **Email:** info@jacobys.co.uk
www.jacobys.co.uk

103 **Just 32**
32 Sun Street, Hitchin, Herts SG5 1AH
Tel: 01462 455666 **Email:** david@just32.com
www.just32.com

104 **Kashu**
9 Hatfield Road, St Albans, Herts AL1 3RR
Tel: 01727 854436 **Email:** info@kashu.co.uk
www.kashu.co.uk

105 **La Stalla Restaurant**
The Green Man, The Green, Clophill, Beds MK45 4AD
Tel: 01525 860352 **Email:** info@lastallarestaurant.co.uk
www.lastallarestaurant.co.uk

106 **The Lion**
70a High Street, Waddesdon, Bucks HP18 0JD
Tel: 01296 651227 **Email:** info@thelionwaddesdon.co.uk

107 **Lussmanns**
Waxhouse Gate, St Albans, Herts AL3 4EW
Tel: 01727 851941 **Email:** chris@lussmanns.com
www.lussmanns.com

108 **Luton Hoo Hotel**
The Mansion House
Luton Hoo
Luton, Bedfordshire
LU1 3TQ
Tel: 01582 698888
Email: reservations@lutonhoo.co.uk
www.lutonhoo.com

109 **The Lytton Arms**
Park Lane, Old Knebworth, Herts SG3 6QB
Tel: 01438 812312 **Email:** info@lyttonarms.co.uk
www.lyttonarms.co.uk

110 **Moggerhanger Park**
Park Road, Moggerhanger, Beds MK44 3RW
Tel: 01767 641007 **Email:** enquiries@moggerhangerpark.com
www.moggerhangerpark.com

111 **Oak Restaurant**
Pendley Manor, Cow Lane, Tring, Herts HP23 5QY
Tel: 01442 891891 **Email:** reception@pendley-manor.co.uk
www.pendley-manor.co.uk

112 **The Old Swan**
58 High Street, Cheddington, Nr Leighton Buzzard, Beds LU7 0RQ
Tel: 01296 668226 **Email:** info@theoldswancheddington.co.uk
www.theoldswancheddington.co.uk

113 **The Old Thatched Inn**
Main Street, Adstock, Bucks MK18 2JN
Tel: 01296 712584 **Email:** enquiries@theoldthatchedinn.co.uk
www.theoldthatchedinn.co.uk

114 **Paris House**
Woburn Park
Woburn
Bedfordshire
MK17 9QP
Tel: 01525 290692
Email: info@parishouse.co.uk
www.parishouse.co.uk

115 **The Plough Restaurant**
Kimbolton Road, Bolnhurst, Beds MK44 2EX
Tel: 01234 376274 **Email:** theplough@bolnhurst.com
www.bolnhurst.com

116 **Passage to India**
10-11 Cofferidge Close, Stony Stratford, Milton Keynes MK11 1BY
Tel: 01908 561999
www.passage2indiatakeaway.co.uk

117 **The Red Chilli**
9 High Street, Buckingham, Bucks MK18 1NT
Tel: 01280 822226
www.redchilligold.com

118 **Redcoats Farmhouse Hotel & Restaurant**
Redcoats Green, Nr Hitchin, Herts SG4 7JR
Tel: 01438 729500 **Email:** info@redcoats.co.uk
www.redcoats.co.uk

119 **The Red Lion**
36 Bridle Path, Brafield-on-the-Green, Northants NN7 1BP
Tel: 01604 890707 **Email:** theredlion@mcmanuspub.co.uk
www.theredlionbrafield.co.uk

120 **The Red Lion**
89 High Street, Yardley Hastings, Northants NN7 1ER
Tel: 01604 696210 **Email:** info@redlionatyardleyhastings.co.uk
www.redliionatyardleyhastings.co.uk

121 **The Red Lion Hotel**
Main Street, East Haddon, Northants NN6 8BU
Tel: 01604 770223 **Email:** nick@redlioneasthaddon.co.uk
www.redlioneasthaddon.co.uk

122 **The Restaurant at Tewin Bury Farm**
B1000 Hertford Road, Nr Welwyn, Herts AL6 0JB
Tel: 01438 717793 **Email:** restaurant@tewinbury.co.uk
www.tewinbury.co.uk

123 **The Robin Hood**
Clifton Reynes, Bucks MK46 5DR
Tel: 01234 711574
www.therobinhoodpub.co.uk

124 **Robinsons**
18-20 St John Street, Newport Pagnell, Bucks MK16 8HJ
Tel: 01908 611400 **Email:** info@robinsonsrestaurant.co.uk
www.robinsonsrestaurant.co.uk

125 **The Royal Oak**
Frieth Road, Bovingdon Green, Nr Marlow, Bucks SL7 2JF
Tel: 01628 488611 **Email:** info@royaloakmarlow.co.uk
www.royaloakmarlow.co.uk

126 **The Royal Oak**
4 Biggleswade Road, Potton, Beds SG19 2LU
Tel: 01767 261888 **Email:** enquiries@theroyaloakpotton.co.uk
www.theroyaloakpotton.co.uk

127 **The Russell Arms**
2 Chalkshires Road, Butlers Cross, Ellesborough, Bucks HP17 0TS
Tel: 01296 622618 **Email:** info@therussellarms.com
www.therussellarms.com

128 **The Saracen's Head**
Main Street, Little Brington, Northants NN7 4HS
Tel: 01604 770640 **Email:** info@yeoldesaracenshead.co.uk
www.thesaracensatbrington.co.uk

129 **The Silk Road**
151 Grafton Gate East, Central Milton Keynes, Bucks MK9 1AE
Tel: 01908 200522 **Email:** enquiries@thesilkroadrestaurants.co.uk
www.thesilkroadrestaurants.co.uk

130 **The Silver Cup**
St Albans Road, Harpenden, Herts AL5 2JF
Tel: 01582 713095 **Email:** info@silvercup.co.uk
www.silvercup.co.uk

131 **Spice of Bruerne**
5 The Canalside, Stoke Bruerne, Northants NN12 7SB
Tel: 01604 863330 **Email:** mail@spiceofbruerne.co.uk
www.spiceofbruerne.com

132 **The Stag Inn**
The Green, Mentmore, Beds LU7 0QF
Tel: 01296 668423 **Email:** info@thestagmentmore.com
www.thestagmentmore.com

133 **St Michaels Manor**
Fishpool Street, St Albans, Herts AL3 4RY
Tel: 01727 864444
www.stmichaelsmanor.com

134 **The Sun at Northaw**
Judges Hill, Northaw, Potters Bar, Herts EN6 4NL
Tel: 01707 655507 **Email:** info@thesunatnorthaw.co.uk
www.thesunatnorthaw.co.uk

135 **The Swan at Lamport**
Harborough Road, Lamport, Northants NN6 9EZ
Tel: 01604 686555 **Email:** theswanlamport@mcmanuspub.co.uk
www.theswanlamport.co.uk

136 **The Swan**
2 Wavendon Road, Salford, Bucks MK17 8BD
Tel: 01908 281008 **Email:** swan@peachpubs.com
www.swansalford.co.uk

137 **The Tree at Cadmore**
Marlow Road, Cadmore End, High Wycombe, Bucks HP14 3PF
Tel: 01494 881183 **Email:** cadmore@treehotel.co.uk
www.cadmore.treehotel.co.uk

138 **Tudor Oaks Lodge Restaurant**
Taylors Road, Astwick, Nr Hitchin, Herts SG5 4AZ
Tel: 01462 888050 **Email:** bookings@tudoroaks.co.uk
www.tudoroakslodge.rtrk.co.uk

139 **Villiers of Buckingham**
3 Castle Street, Buckingham, Bucks MK18 1BS
Tel: 01280 822444 **Email:** villiers@oxfordshire-hotels.co.uk
www.villiers-hotel.co.uk

140 **The Wharf**
Cornhill Lane, Bugbrooke, Northants NN7 3QB
Tel: 01604 832585 **Email:** rich@the-wharf.co.uk
www.the-wharf.co.uk

141 **White Hart**
Ampthill Road, Maulden, Beds MK45 2DH
Tel: 01525 406118 **Email:** info@whitehartmaulden.com
www.whitehartsaladcart.com

142 **The White Hart**
1 Gun Lane, Sherington, Newport Pagnell, Bucks MK16 9PE
Tel: 01908 611953 **Email:** whitehartresort@aol.com
www.whitehartsherington.com

143 **The White Horse**
White Horse Lane, Burnham Green, Nr Welwyn, Herts AL6 0HA
Tel: 01438 798100
www.whitehorseburnhamgreen.com

144 **The Windhover**
Brampton Lane, Chapel Brampton, Northampton NN6 8AA
Tel: 01604 847859
www.vintageinn.co.uk

145 **Woburn Brasserie**
13 Bedford Street, Woburn, Beds MK17 9QB
Tel: 01525 290260 **Email:** info@woburnbrasserie.co.uk
www.woburnbrasserie.co.uk

146 **The Worlds End**
Ecton, Northants NN6 0QN
Tel: 01604 414521 **Email:** info@theworldsend.org
www.theworldsend.org

147 **Ye Olde Swan**
Newport Road, Woughton on the Green, Milton Keynes, Bucks MK6 3BS
Tel: 01908 679489 **Email:** reza.najafi@pubandkitchenco.com
www.pubandkitchenco.com

148 **Ye Three Fyshes**
Bridge Street, Turvey, Beds MK43 8ER
Tel: 01234 881463 **Email:** info@yethreefyshes.co.uk
www.yethreefyshes.co.uk

149 **The Zodiac Restaurant**
Hanbury Manor Hotel, Ware, Herts SG12 0SD
Tel: 01920 487722
www.marriott.co.uk

If you have dined at a restaurant that you think we should know about then please let us know!

Your recommendations ensure only good restaurants appear in THE FOODIE GUIDE

Reservations

Use this space to record details of your restaurant bookings

Restaurant	Date	Time	No. of people	Comments

The Purple Goose Restaurant

Candied Lime and Blueberry Posset with Lemon Thyme Infusion

Chef Profile

Describe your style of cooking
Modern British.

Current Speciality
Fresh Fish and Pork Belly.

Training and background
Formerly at The Paris House, Knife & Cleaver, Eat Fish and The White Hart.

What's the best advice you have ever been given?
Work hard and all things in moderation - including moderation!

What food would you say is good value for money?
Fresh fish and steaks.

What is your favourite comfort food?
Pick 'N' Mix Sweets!

What latest food trends are you into?
Innovative cutting edge desserts.

Which chef do you admire most?
Heston Blumenthal.

Do you think Britain's culinary reputation has advanced in recent years?
Yes, through the emergence of several British chefs as industry leading stars.

Scott Ludlow

In The Kitchen

Ingredients - Serves 4

- 300ml Double Cream
- 6 tbsp Caster Sugar
- 6 Limes (juiced)
- Zest of Lime
- 9 Sprigs of Lemon Thyme
- Stock Syrup (sugar and water syrup)

Method

1. Slowly bring the cream, sugar and lemon thyme sprigs to the boil. Boil vigorously for 2 minutes while stirring continuously. Remove from heat and stir in the lime juice, then remove sprigs.
2. Put the mixture into ramekins and cool in a fridge for 90 minutes. The mixture should be firm but not too solid.
3. In the meantime boil the lime zest in the sugar syrup and decorate the chilled posset with the zest and blueberries.

Chef Profile

Describe your style of cooking
The use of local seasonal ingredients has always been the inspiration for my cooking. Gastro Pub and Modern British are terms I don't really like. I just like using great ingredients delivered to us by people we know and doing justice to the great products our suppliers give us.

Current speciality
Roast Suckling Pig Three Ways - Cutlet, Slowly Roasted Leg, Sausage made with Braised Shoulder, Gratin Potatoes with Chimney Smoked Bacon & Suckling Pig Belly, Apple & Calvados Jelly, Spring Greens, Raisins and Garlic.

Training and background
Worked with Gordon Ramsay, Marcus Wareing, Angela Hartnett, Sally Clarke, Stephen Bull, Nicole Farhi.

What's the best advice you have ever been given?
Great ingredients, cooked simply, make the best dishes.

What is your favourite comfort food?
Pizza and a glass of wine.

What latest food trends are you into?
The food trends now are to grow your own, local food and knowing your suppliers personally. Funny how trends go around in circles as we have been doing that for 10 years.

Which chef do you admire most?
Marco Pierre White. His first book "White Heat" was and still is an inspiration.

The Crooked Billet

Emma Gilchrist

In The Kitchen

Ingredients - Serves 4

- 8 Digestive Biscuits
- 35g Melted Butter
- 250g White Chocolate
- 125g Double Cream
- 2 Punnets Fresh Raspberries, English Please!!

Optional Easy Raspberry Sauce:

- 1 Punnet of Raspberries
- 2tbsp Caster Sugar
- Juice of one Lemon

Method

1. Crush the digestives and combine with the melted butter.
2. Divide the mix into 4 and press into 4 metal rings. If you do not have rings a cake tin or pie dish is great.
3. Place the white chocolate in a glass bowl and melt over a pan of hot water, stirring occasionally.
4. When the chocolate has melted add the cream and stir.
5. Gently fold in most of the raspberries, retaining some for a garnish.
6. Pour the mixture into the rings or cake tin. Allow to cool and refrigerate.
7. When needed remove from the ring or tin, place a few fresh raspberries on top and serve.

Optional Easy Raspberry Sauce:

1. In a food processor blitz all the ingredients together.
2. Strain through a sieve and serve.

White Chocolate Raspberry Cheesecake

The Betsey Wynne

Chef Profile

Describe your style of cooking
Old English but with a modern interpretation.

Current Speciality
Steaks, Pies and Casseroles.

Training and background
Originally trained in Leeds, C&Gs Standard. Owned and operated successful Pubs and Restaurants.

What's the best advice you have ever been given?
You are only as good as your last meal.

What food would you say is good value for money?
The Lamb Rump and Swanbourne Beef.

What is your favourite comfort food?
Roast Lamb.

What latest food trends are you into?
Sourcing local and grow your own food.

Which chef do you admire the most?
Anton Mosimann.

Do you think Britain's culinary reputation has advanced in recent years?
Yes, I feel it has always been good.

Kevin Close

In The Kitchen

Ingredients - Serves 4

- 750g Venison Loin
- 50g each: Diced Onion, Carrot, Celery & Leeks
- 1 Clove of Garlic
- 6 Juniper Berries
- 4 fl oz Orange Juice & Red Wine
- 2 tbsp Honey
- 2 tbsp Redcurrant Jelly
- 6 fl oz Beef Stock
- Zest of Orange & Segments for decoration
- 2 Lavender Stems
- 200g Washed Baby Spinach
- 200g Caramelized Onions
- 400g Cooked Potatoes for Sautéing
- 2 Sprigs Thyme

Method

1. Fry the diced vegetables until light brown. Add red wine, juniper and garlic and reduce by half.
2. Add orange juice, beef stock, redcurrent jelly, honey and one sprig of lavender.
3. Simmer until syrup in texture then sieve into a jug.
4. Strip loin of any sinews, then season, place in a hot pan with a little olive oil rubbed into the meat.
5. When brown all over, place in a hot oven, gas mark 7 / 220ºC / 425ºF for 5-6 minutes, allow to rest.
6. Fry the onions, add cooked potatoes, season and add some fresh thyme. Wilt spinach and drain, lightly butter and season.
7. *Construct dish in 4 stages:* 1 Press sauté potatoes into a large ring, top with spinach, place on a serving plate and remove the ring. 2 Carve loin and place on the top of the spinach. 3 Dress with orange segments and zest. 4 Spoon over the sauce and decorate with the lavender flowers.

Venison Loin with Juniper and Lavender Jus

Chef Profile

Describe your style of cooking
Modern and Classical British Cuisine with International influence.

Current speciality
Using the produce from Claydon's kitchen garden and making jellies and chutneys.

Training and background
Top hotels in London and ending the training at The Montreux Palace, Switzerland. Head Chef RAC Club, Pall Mall, The London Stock Exchange, Langan's and Rosamund the Fair, Oxford's famous cruising restaurant.

What's the best advice you have ever been given?
Everyone is important in the team, from the kitchen porter to Head Chef.

What food would you say is good value for money?
Pork Fillet.

What is your favourite comfort food?
Roast lunch.

What latest food trends are you into?
Keeping it real. In the back-to-basics economy perhaps it is natural to return to basic ingredients. This isn't about retro, or comfort food or even cost it's about determining the essentials and stocking your pantry accordingly. It's about pure, simple, clear and sustainable.

Which chef do you admire most?
Alexis Soyer (The Jamie Oliver of the 1850's).

Do you think Britain's culinary reputation has advanced in recent years?
Yes, I believe the British are leading the way!

Tim Matthews

The Carriage House Restaurant, Claydon House

In The Kitchen

Ingredients - Serves 10

For the Meringue:
- 4 Egg Whites
- 250g Sugar
- 1 Pinch Salt

For the Biscuit:
- 150g Unsalted Butter
- 90g Icing Sugar
- 1 Small Egg (beaten)
- 250g Plain Flour

For the Lemon Cream:
- 2 tbsp Cornflour
- 100g Golden Caster Sugar
- Juice of 5 Lemons
- Zest of 2 Lemons
- 2 Egg Yolks
- 200ml Double Cream

For the Citrus Syrup:
- 700g Caster Sugar
- 1ltr Water
- Juice of 2 Lemons
- Juice of 2 Limes
- Juice of 2 Oranges

Method

For the Meringue: 1 Whisk egg whites till they form soft peaks then gradually add the sugar and salt continually whisking. Whisk the mixture until it forms stiff peaks. 2 Pipe the meringue mixture into disks on baking parchment then place in an oven preheated to 110°C for 1 hour.

For the Citrus Syrup: 1 Place all ingredients in a pan and place on the heat. Bring up to the boil then reduce to a simmer for an hour or until syrup contistency.

For the Lemon Curd: 1 Place the cornflour, caster sugar, juice and zest of lemons in a pan and thicken slowly on the stove then leave to cool. 2 Once cool, whisk in the egg yolks.

For the Biscuit: 1 Cream butter and sugar together until pale and light, add egg, then mix in flour to make a biscuit dough then chill for 30 minutes. 2 Roll out and cut to desired shape and bake in the oven for 15 minutes.

To assemble: 1 Whip the cream until stiff and add 2 tablespoons of the lemon curd mixture. Then combine the rest of the curd mixture with the cream. 2 On a large plate place one meringue disk at the bottom, put a spoonful of the lemon cream mixture on top, then place one of the biscuits, another spoonful of lemon cream and another meringue disk, then another spoonful of lemon cream and finally drizzle some of the citrus syrup over the stack and around the plate.

Lemon Meringue Stack

Cameron's, The Navigation Inn

Chef Profile

Describe your style of cooking
Modern British. Also enjoy traditional British and Modern European.

Current speciality
Enjoy cooking fresh fish and shellfish. Using wild products such as Wild Garlic Leaf and sea vegetables such as Samphire, Sea Purslane and Sea Beets.

Training and background
Gordon Ramsay's Boxwood Café (22 months), Scott's of Mayfair 2 ½ years).

What's the best advice you have ever been given?
When at Boxwood Café I was constantly shouted at, which I thought was because I was doing everything wrong. My Senior Chef De Partie told me that it was because he liked me and pushed me hard to do well. If I was ignored, then that was a bad sign.

What food would you say is good value for money?
Using unusual cuts of meat and the braising meats to make fantastic tasting dishes.

What is your favourite comfort food?
Ribeye on the bone. If it is nice weather barbequing it is the best.

Which chef do you admire most?
Stuart Gillies who was my head chef at Boxwood Café, Kevin Gratton who was my head chef at Scott's. Both trained me in the early parts of my career.

Do you think Britain's culinary reputation has advanced in recent years?
Yes, London is the gastronomic capital of the world. All the top chefs work there. Lots of other areas have many Michelin restaurants.

Mark Adcock

In The Kitchen

Ingredients - Serves 6

- 220ml Fresh Lemon Juice (4 lemons)
- 840ml Double Cream
- 240g Caster Sugar
- Fresh Berries (strawberries, raspberries, blueberries)

Method

1. Zest the lemons with a fine grater.
2. Squeeze the juice out of the lemons and keep in a separate jug.
3. In a heavy based saucepan add the lemon zest with the cream and sugar.
4. Bring slowly to the boil, when boiling turn down the heat and simmer for 4 minutes.
5. Add the lemon juice and whisk.
6. Pour the mixture through a sieve into a jug.
7. Skim off the froth with a ladle, then pour into glasses.
8. Put the glasses in the fridge to set for at least 8 hours.
9. When set, place the berries on top. Alternatively, put the berries in the glass before adding the mixture.

Lemon Posset with Mixed Berries

Chef Profile

Describe your style of cooking

A modern twist on classic French cooking techniques, with a large Spanish influence.

Training and background

I started working as a chef part time in 2000. Upon deciding to go in to cooking as a career I completed a full diploma course at Leith's School of Food and Wine in London, leaving with honours in 2003. Upon completion I went on to work at some of London's top restaurants.

What food would you say is good value for money?

It can be anything from a quality homemade burger that costs you £5 to a massively expensive tasting menu . Value for money is different for everyone. For me as long as the quality is there, in relation to the price then I am happy.

What latest food trends are you into?

I am experimenting a lot with my water bath at the moment, it's great for slow cooking whilst keeping clean fresh flavours. Now though it's time to start trying to create food trends rather than follow existing ones!

Do you think Britain's culinary reputation has advanced in recent years?

Massively so. Thanks to top British Chefs like Heston Blumenthal, Gordon Ramsay and Marcus Wareing, amongst others the UK can boast some of the world's best restaurants. TV personalities like Jamie Oliver, Hugh Fearnley-Whittingstall and more recently some of the afore-mentioned chefs have helped raise awareness that food is more than just a fuel source. It's something we all depend upon to live so lets embrace it. Enjoy it and be inspired by it.

Dan Cameron

In The Kitchen

Ingredients

- 275ml Fromage Frais
- 1 rounded teaspoon Cornflour
- 4 large Egg Yolks
- 75g Golden Caster Sugar
- 475ml Milk
- Half a Vanilla Pod and Beans

Method

1. Bring milk, vanilla and sugar to the boil.
2. Whisk yolks and cornflour together until you have a smooth paste.
3. Check all your sugar has dissolved. Pour milk mixture over eggs and stir until combined.
4. Return mix to a pan and stir continuously over a low heat until the mixture begins to thicken.
5. Remove from the heat and pass through a fine sieve into a bowl.
6. Cool the mixture down by placing the bowl in a container of ice water until it is at room temperature.
7. Fold Fromage Frais into mix and follow your ice cream machine manufacturers instructions.

At Cameron's the Fromage Frais Ice Cream is served with slow cooked Apricots, Pain D'épices, Apricot Jelly and Pink Peppercorn and Bay Leaf Syrup.

Cameron's, The Navigation Inn

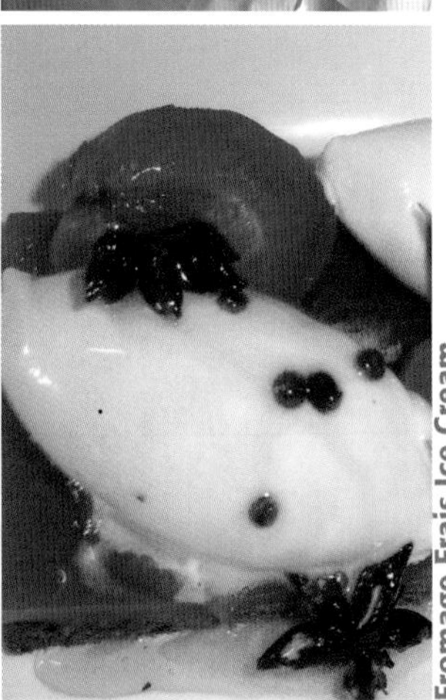

Fromage Frais Ice Cream

The Nags Head, Great Missenden

Mackerel Escabeche with Grilled Jersey Royals & English Asparagus

Chef Profile

Describe your style of cooking
Classical French cooking with a Modern British twist.

Current speciality
Baked American Cheesecake with Blueberry Compote.

Training and background
Academy of Culinary Arts Diploma - Poole & Bournemouth College. 4 years working for Roux Fine Dining - Albert Roux's company now run by Michelle Roux Jnr.

What's the best advice you have ever been given?
Be nice to your Mother.

What food would you say is good value for money?
Eggs. They are invaluable in a kitchen, they're used so regularly.

What is your favourite comfort food?
Beans on toast.

What latest food trends are you into?
I like the combination of hot and cold together. A hot Smoked Chicken and Sweetcorn Pureé Risotto with cold beetroot. Salsa is a good example.

Which chef do you admire most?
Albert Roux because, "Flavour is of the utmost importance".

Do you think Britain's culinary reputation has advanced in recent years?
Yes definitely - the celebrity chef scene has definitely helped make cooking a more desirable job to newcomers. It has also helped to push people to become more competitive.

Howard Gale

In The Kitchen

Ingredients - Serves 2

- 2 x 150g Mackerel Fillets
- Sea Salt
- White Pepper
- Olive Oil
- Knob of Butter
- Flour for dusting (prevents skin sticking to the pan)

Escabeche:

- 1 Banana Shallot
- 1 Red Pepper
- 1 Yellow Pepper
- 1 Carrot
- 1 Lemon
- 1 Orange
- 3 tbsp White Wine Vinegar
- 3 tbsp Extra Virgin Olive Oil
- 1 tsp Coriander Seeds
- 3 tbsp Chopped Coriander
- Pinch of Saffron (optional)

Garnish:

- Asparagus
- Jersey Royal Potatoes
- Rocket Salad

Method

1. Slice the shallot into thin rings, julienne (cut into match stick size pieces) the pepper, carrot and zest from the lemon and orange and set aside.
2. In a separate pan add the juice from the lemon and orange. Add the white wine vinegar, coriander seeds, saffron and olive oil and bring to a simmer. Add all the sliced ingredients and cook for a further 3 minutes.
3. Cook the asparagus and the Jersey Royals and refresh in cold water.
4. *For the Mackerel*: Heat a pan with oil, season the fish (flesh side) and dust the skin with the flour. Quickly fry the fish skin side down, then turn the fish and add the knob of butter. Cook for a further 20 seconds when the butter is bubbling on a low heat. Remove the fish and pour the hot escabeche over the fish and leave for 5 - 10 minutes.
5. Heat the asparagus and if possible cut and grill the Jersey potatoes and arrange on a plate. Place the fish on the asparagus and garnish with the hot escabeche and vegetables.

Chef Profile

Describe your style of cooking
Traditional British most of the time but I do love fusion food and often introduce spices and flavours from around the world.

Current speciality
Different char-grilled kebabs on large hanging stands. They are so versatile as you can use any combination of marinated meat, fish and veg you like. As well as the great fresh tastes you can offer it adds a bit of theatre to a meal.

Training and background
Started as a kitchen porter and worked my way through college and different sections in local restaurants meaning most of my training has been hands on "on the job".

What's the best advice you have ever been given?
Don't run with knives, listen to the boss and to what your customer wants.

What food would you say is good value for money?
Lamb Shoulder and Belly Pork, they can have so much flavour if cooked sympathetically and sourced from good suppliers. Chicken livers is another food I think is great value and massively under-used.

What is your favourite comfort food?
Banoffee Cheesecake - with extra toffee sauce.

What latest food trends are you into?
Taking those cheaper cuts of meat and making something special with them. It may take a little longer, but the taste is worth it in the end.

Which chef do you admire most?
Gordon Ramsay. I recently had the opportunity to tour one of his kitchens during service and dine at the restaurant. His philosophy of treating food with respect (even if he doesn't always do that with his staff) and caring where things are sourced from shone through in all the dishes served.

Mark Wood

The Plough at Simpson

In The Kitchen

Ingredients - Serves 4

- 4 x 150g Chicken Breasts
- 120g Goats Cheese
- 100g Wilted Spinach
- 8 slices Parma Ham

For the Salsa:

- ½ Yellow Pepper
- 1 small White Onion (diced)
- 12 Cherry Tomatoes (halved)
- 1 small Red Chilli (finely chopped)
- 1 tbsp White Sugar
- 1 tbsp Balsamic Vinegar
- 10g Flat Leaf Parsley (roughly chopped)
- 10g Basil (roughly chopped)
- ½ a Lemon (squeezed)
- Salt & Pepper to taste

Method

1. Pierce a hole through each breast and stuff with a mixture of goats cheese and spinach. Lightly season the breast and wrap two slices of Parma ham around each one. These can be rolled in cling film and placed in the fridge. Ideal for making in advance for dinner parties.
2. *For the Salsa:* Gently fry the pepper, onion and chilli for a couple of minutes adding cherry tomatoes and sugar then fry for another minute until soft but still left with a slight crunch. Add herbs, lemon juice and vinegar and season to taste. This can again be prepared in advance and cooled and placed in the fridge.
3. Take the chicken out of the fridge 20 minutes before you are ready to cook and pre-heat the oven to approx 200°C /Gas 6. When the oven is hot remove cling film and drizzle chicken with some olive oil and place in the oven for approx 18-20 minutes.
4. Once chicken is cooked remove from oven and allow 3-4 minutes resting time. *For the Straw Potatoes:* Meanwhile, peel and grate 2 potatoes (do not wash the potatoes as the starch helps them to slightly stick together and gives them body on the plate). During this time you can gently re-heat the Salsa and the Straw Potatoes can be deep fried for 30-40 seconds or until golden. Place onto kitchen paper and lightly season.
5. Now you are ready to plate your dish. Take 4 warm plates and place some Straw Potatoes into the middle of each, place four spoonfuls of Salsa around the potatoes. Slice chicken down the middle at an angle, place on top of potatoes and serve.

Breast of Chicken stuffed with Goats Cheese

Olivier's Restaurant at The Inn at Woburn

Chef Profile

Describe your style of cooking
A mixture of classic French and British with a twist.

Current speciality
Woburn Venison - at the moment we have a Carpaccio on the menu with a basil crust and parmesan crisps.

Training and background
I trained in France for 10 years and then moved to England, working in mainly country house hotels including Relais & Chateau.

What's the best advice you have ever been given?
Always taste and more importantly, enjoy what you are cooking!

What food would you say is good value for money?
Fresh food - you can find real bargains and great quality locally produced food at local markets.

What is your favourite comfort food?
It's got to be chocolate - every time. Dark is definitely the best.

What latest food trends are you into?
Purées, either fruit or vegetable. The smoother they are, the easier they are to work with.

Which chef do you most admire?
The Roux brothers. They trained so many great chefs such as Marco Pierre White and Gordon Ramsay.

Do you think Britain's culinary reputation has advanced in recent years?
Yes definitely. Speaking as a Frenchman I think that France no longer has the monopoly on good chefs!

Olivier Bertho

In The Kitchen

Ingredients

- Venison Loin
- Parmesan Crisps
- Basil Oil
- Basil Salt
- Rocket leaves to garnish

For the Basil Salt:
- 2 boxes Maldon salt
- 170g Fresh Basil leaves (2 bunches)
- 1 tbsp Roasted Juniper Berries
- 1 tbsp Pink Peppercorns

For the Basil Oil:
- Fresh Basil leaves (1 bunch)
- 200ml Pomace oil
- Juice of 1 lemon
- Salt and pepper

Method

For the Basil Salt: 1 Blitz the basil leaves into a paste with the peppercorn and juniper berries. 2 Rub the paste into the salt and place onto a flat tray. 3 Bake for an hour at 120ºC stirring often. This should take an hour maximum to dry it well. When cool, store in an airtight container.
For the Venison: 1 Prepare and trim well of all sinew. 2 Mix some salt and cayenne pepper and rub well into the piece of loin, clingfilm tight then vac pack before freezing the piece in individual bags. 3 Slice when still frozen with a slicing machine or very sharp knife, be careful and take your time. Allow 5 or 6 slices per portion.
For the Parmesan Crisps: 1 Blitz Parmesan shavings in a mixer. 2 Place an oval shaped cutter on greaseproof paper on a baking tray, and fill with the Parmesan crumbs. 3 Place under the grill (low shelf), until they become gold but not too brown. 4 Let them cool slightly, then place on the back of a terrine to get them in the right shape, reserved in an airtight container.
For the Basil Oil: 1 Blitz in the Thermo mix or jug mixer the Pomace oil, 1 bunch of basil leaves (just the leaves), the lemon juice and salt and pepper, on speed 10 for 40 seconds, then drain through a fine muslin.
To serve: First place the Parmesan crisps in the centre of the plate and lay the venison slices around this. Place the rocket leaves on top of the Parmesan crisps and then drizzle the basil oil around the edge.

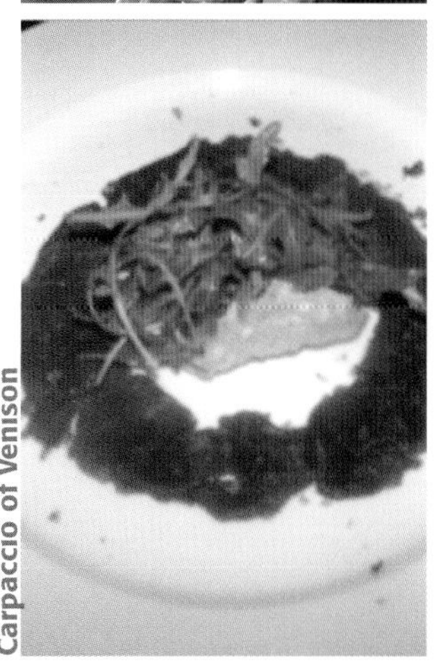
Carpaccio of Venison

Chef Profile

Describe your style of cooking
A mix of modern and classic English food.

Current speciality
Roasted Aylesbury Duckling, Apple Sauce with Calvados and Sage and Onion Stuffing. This has been our speciality for a long time.

Training and brackground
Started my training at The Kings Head then moved on to Grosvenor House Park Lane, Randolph Oxford, Pendley Manor (Sous Chef), Le Belle Epoque South Kensington (Sous Chef), Head Chef Brocket Hall Golf Club, Senior Sous Chef Auberge Du Lac.

What's the best advice you have ever been given?
Shut up and listen and keep your head down.

What is your favourite comfort food?
Mothers Sunday Roast followed by Apple Pie and Vanilla Ice Cream.

What latest food trends are you into?
I don't follow trends, I don't work for a guide. I do what I believe in and what I think our clientele will enjoy. There is always room for my style of cooking. Trends come and go along with restaurants.

Which chef do you admire most?
Gordon Ramsay, he has done good for the trade (and some bad), overall though a very talented cook and to achieve what he has achieved in a small amount of time is pretty amazing.

Do you think Britain's culinary reputation has advanced in recent years?
Yes it has but has also been there for a very long time. The last few years chefs have been in the media spotlight and this has brought them to the masses.

The Kings Head, Ivinghoe

In The Kitchen

Ingredients - Serves 4 - 6

- 2 Whole Eggs
- 6 Egg Yolks
- 1 Vanilla Pod
- 250g Sugar
- 30g Demerara Sugar
- 300ml Milk
- 300ml Double Cream
- 50g Soft Butter
- 8 Slices of Bread
- 150g Sultanas
- Ovenproof dish 220 x 200 mm

Method

1. Split the vanilla pod and remove seeds. Finely chop the husk, add to the milk and boil.
2. Whisk egg yolks, eggs and sugar, continue whisking adding cream mixture and pass through a sieve.
3. Butter bread, take off crusts and cut in half.
4. Butter mould with butter paper and lay down half the sultanas followed by half the bread and repeat this procedure one more time.
5. Pour egg custard over the bread, push down on bread to make sure it is submerged.
6. Place in a tray filled with 200mm of water. Bake at 175°C / 325°F / Gas mark 4 for approx 1 hour until custard is set, sprinkle with demerara sugar and caramelise with a blow torch. Serve with ice-cream, cream or custard.

Bread and Butter Pudding

Galloway's Woburn

Chef Profile

Describe your style of cooking
We have an eclectic mix of styles but always able to adapt and move with ideas from our customers. We are a team always striving to improve!!

Current speciality
Gressingham Duck Breast in a Black Cherry Sauce, Rösti Potato and Fresh Vegetable Mix.

Training and background
Started at The Red Lion washing up while still at school then at Galloways for the past 13 years, including an apprenticeship through Bedford College.

What's the best advice you have ever been given?
I have always worked with the view that what the customer wants, he gets, i.e. the menu is a list of ingredients we have, if they want to change it, we do our best, without customers we don't survive - simple as that.

What food would you say is good value for money?
Local pork and fresh fish, we get delivered daily from Brixham.

What latest food trends are you into?
Local produce! and recently working on new ideas with Simon at Best Butchers, such as the wonderful Smoked Rib Eye Steak and Gluten Free Sausages for our BBQ Specials.

Which chef do you admire most?
Swedish guy from The Muppets and Peter Chandler.

Comments
As an independent, Galloway's has been able to survive everything that group owned operators have thrown at us. We still survive and keep busy by remembering who is number one - you the customer!!

Kevin Newell

In The Kitchen

Ingredients

- 7 Egg Yolks
- 5oz Caster Sugar
- 1 pint Whipping Cream
- A few drops of Vanilla Essence
- Demerara Sugar to glaze

Method

1. Mix the egg yolks and the caster sugar together.
2. Pour in the cream and mix well.
3. Stir in a few drops of vanilla essence.
4. Pour the mixture into ramekins and place into a deep tray.
5. Fill the tray with warm water about halfway up the side of the ramekins.
6. Place the tray onto the griddle or a low gas ring and bring the water to the boil.
7. Once the water has boiled put the tray in the oven and cook at 150ºC for 45 minutes to one hour (a cooked brulée should wobble and the top should spring back when touched).
8. When cooked take the brulées and wipe clean the ramekins and place in the fridge to cool.
9. Before serving coat the top of the brulée in a thin layer of demerara sugar and caramelise under the grill or using a gas gun.

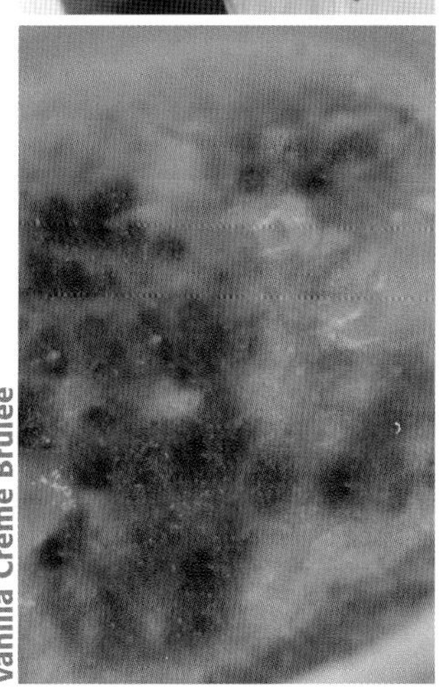
Vanilla Crème Brulée

Chef Profile

Describe your style of cooking
Our food is very seasonal and is a mixture of English, French and Italian.

Current speciality
Chefs Evenings. Guests pay what they think the food was worth. Have trust in your chefs to deliver. You've trained them, so no matter how young they are, have faith in them. I do and it works!

Training and background
I am self taught. I was Head Chef in London at 20, Executive Chef at 30 and now at 40 owner and operator. Maybe at 50 TV beckons. I've always had aims and goals and achieved them so far.

What's the best advice you have ever been given?
Keep it simple and know your customers.

What food would you say is good value for money?
Always seasonal products especially if there is a glut due to the weather. Our local organic farm phones us if they have an excess of fruit or vegetables, as was the case with strawberries this year (and rabbits!).

What is your favourite comfort food?
Fresh ingredient Club Sandwich. If made right it beats the best food. Not many places do it now, when was the last time you saw it on a menu?

What latest food trends are you into?
Retro. We're taking from the past and adapting to our customers tastes today. Best-sellers are Boiled Smoked Bacon, Parsley Sauce, Mash and Greens. And Salmon, Cod and Crab Fishcakes with a Pea and Mustard Sauce.

Which chef do you admire most?
Keith Floyd for his passion for food and life. He always took risks and failed at times but always came back and never failed to entertain.

Darron Smith

Horse & Jockey

In The Kitchen

Ingredients - Serves 4

- 2 kg Pork Belly - Bone In
  (The better the breed of pig the more crispy the skin)
- 2 pinch Maldon Salt
- 2 pinch Cracked Black Pepper
- Olive Oil
- 4 large Carrots cut into 4
- 2 large Parsnips cut into 4
- 1 Swede *(roughly cut)*
- 8 Baby Beetroot *(leave whole)*

Method

1 Score the skin of the pork.
2 Rub with olive oil and sprinkle with the salt and pepper.
3 Place in roasting tray in middle of oven for 1¾ hours at 180ºc.
4 Whilst pork is cooking blanch vegetables (beetroot separately) and drain when soft.
5 Place in roasting tray and coat with olive oil and sprinkle a pinch of salt and pepper over vegetables.
6 Cook for 1 hour at 180ºc.
7 After 1¾ hours raise oven to maximum and cook pork for further 15 mins.
8 Leave to rest for 5 mins out of oven.
9 Cut into 4 and serve surrounded with vegetables and sauce of your choice.

Crispy Pork Belly with

The Wollaston Inn

Chef Profile

Describe your style of cooking
Modern British, Seasonal Menus with everything made in-house.

Current Speciality
Fresh daily seafood always a speciality, also New Spring Lamb Rump and a Lamb Shoulder and Goats Cheese Wellington.

What's the best advice you have ever been given?
If you can read you can learn and achieve anything - keep up to date and keep learning.

What food would you say is good value for money?
Free range pork products - you can use everything; ears, cheeks, belly and traditional cuts and the cost is great along with the flavour.

What is your favourite comfort food?
Shepherds Pie - nothing better with soft mash and rich gravy!

What latest food trends are you into?
Don't really follow trends, however, chefs are being forced to think more about food costs and therefore have to be more resourceful and use seasonal ingredients and different cuts which is good for competitive local suppliers and using more unusual cuts of meat.

Which chef do you admire most?
Any chef in the Country working 15 hour days, creating new menus and loving their job - the unsung chefs, commis and pot washers producing fresh, inventive food.

Do you think Britain's culinary reputation has advanced in recent years?
I think that Britain has established itself firmly at the top of the culinary world. Along with Spain it has chefs using traditional and modern methods and knowledge to take cuisine to that next level.

Chris Spencer

In The Kitchen

Sea Bass and New Potato Salad

Ingredients - Serves 4

- 4 Sea Bass Fillets
- 100g Crayfish Tails
- 200g Smoked Bacon
- 200g Artichoke Hearts
- 150g Green Olives
- 200g Spinach
- 50g Butter
- Juice ½ Lemon
- 1tbsp Chopped Parsley
- Salt & Pepper
- Vegetable Oil

Method

1. Cook off new potatoes in boiling, salted water for 10 minutes. Cool then slice into three.
2. Cook artichoke hearts in boiling water for 4 minutes then dice.
3. Heat a saute pan to a moderate heat, add oil then fry diced bacon. Add sliced new potatoes and brown, then reduce heat.
4. In another pan, heat, add oil then place Sea Bass skin side down and cook for 3 minutes on a medium heat then add butter and lemon juice to the pan. Turn fish over onto flesh side and remove from heat.
5. Increase heat under saute pan to high then add artichokes, Crayfish tails, olives and spinach. Add a little butter and seasoning then when spinach has wilted turn out onto warm plates.
6. Garnish with parsley then place Sea Bass on top.

Chef Profile

Describe your style of cooking
English classic with a French twist.

Current speciality
Pan Fried Fillet of Pork with an Apple and Black Pudding Crumble and a Wild Mushroom Bouillon.

Training and background
5 years at The Bricklayers Arms working with Claude Paillet, 3 years as Senior Sous Chef for Blubeckers and Edwinns Restaurants.

What's the best advice you have ever been given?
You can always add but never take away! (recipes and seasoning).

What food would you say is good value for money?
Less popular cuts of meat cooked really well in different ways (than expected).

What is your favourite comfort food?
A good Steak & Ale Pie (no kidneys!).

What latest food trends are you into?
Sous-Vide (water bath); Re-inventing classics; Slow cooking.

Which chef do you admire most?
Marco Pierre White.

Do you think Britain's culinary reputation has advanced in recent years?
Definitely - supermarkets sell everything you need and television chefs raise public opinions and expectations.

The Bricklayers Arms

David Long

In The Kitchen

Ingredients - Serves 4

- 2 Pork Tenderloins (Fillet)
- 150g Fresh Mixed Wild Mushrooms
- 20g Dried Mushrooms
- 200ml Veg and/or Chicken Bouillon (Fresh or Cube)
- 4 Slices Black Pudding
- 2 Apples (Granny Smith or Bramley are good)
- 100g Butter
- 100g Flour

Method

1 Peel and slice the apples, cook in butter until soft and add the black pudding cut into batons. Place the mixture in 4 small individual dishes.

2 *For the crumble:* Use 100g of flour and 50g of butter and mix with your fingertips until light and crumbly, then cover and bake for 2 minutes on a baking tray.

3 *For the mushroom bouillon:* Soften the dried wild mushrooms in cold water for a few hours and then boil for 10 minutes. Add the cube of stock and blend. Pan fry the wild mushrooms in the remaining butter and add to the bouillon, season to taste.

4 Thinly slice the pork tenderloin and pan fry or grill to your taste. Place on a deep plate or dish and cover with the mushroom bouillon.

5 Serve with the apple and black pudding mixture already warmed up and sprinkled with the crumble.
Enjoy!

Pork Tenderloin in a Mushroom Bouillon with Apple and Black Pudding Crumble

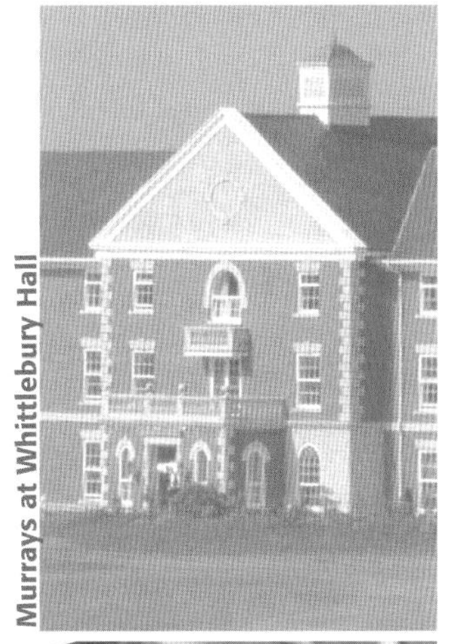

Murrays at Whittlebury Hall

Chef Profile

Describe your style of cooking

Modern seasonal British with international and classical influences.

Current Speciality

Morecambe Bay Saltmarsh Lamb with Basil Mousse, Baby Spinach, Fondant Potatoes and a Thyme Sauce. It's a dish I've been evolving for a few years but have never found a home for it until now.

What's the best advice you have ever been given?

You can never stop learning - every day is a school day.

What food would you say is good value for money?

We have some very underrated native sea fish around our coastline. Think outside of the usual, follow the seasons and you'll be bound to be surprised.

What latest food trends are you into?

I tend not to follow trends, but find my inspiration in old cookbooks as much as I do the latest publications. I cook what I would like to eat myself, not what I think I should be cooking to be fashionable.

Which chef do you admire most?

I admire any chef who tries to make a positive difference to the industry at any level. Whether it's my local pub offering me somewhere nice to go and eat, or higher profile chefs raising awareness of issues such as animal welfare or school dinners.

Do you think Britain's culinary reputation has advanced in recent years?

Most definitely. Across the board, London has become the best capital city to eat out in within the past five years. As an example, cooking programmes are now becoming more relevant and highlight positives such as provenance, trying to stay local and keeping it seasonal. As a nation we have never been more aware of food!

Christian Morris

In The Kitchen

Ingredients - Serves 4

- 12 Hand Dived Scallops (Roe removed)

For the sauce:

- 1kg Chicken Bones/Wings (roasted till brown)
- 1 Carrot (peeled and chopped)
- 1 Onion (peeled and chopped)
- 2 Sticks of Celery (washed and chopped)
- 2 Whole Garlic Cloves (peeled)
- 1 Leek (washed and chopped)
- Sprig of Thyme, Rosemary and 1 Bay Leaf

For the sauce garnish:

- 1 peeled, deseeded Beef Tomato (cut into same size squares)
- Equal quantities of chopped Tarragon, Parsley, Chives & Chervil

For the Purée:

- 1 head of Cauliflower (chopped)
- 30g Butter
- Milk to cover
- Pinch of Salt & Pepper

For the Florets:

- 8 same size pieces of Cauliflower
- 100g Flour
- 25g Corn Flour
- 1 tsp Baking Powder
- Sparkling Water
- Pinch of Salt

Salad garnish:

- Mixture of Micro Herbs, Pea Shoots and Curly Endive

Method

For the sauce: Place all ingredients in a suitable size pan, bring to the boil and simmer for 3 hours. Strain the liquid through a fine sieve and remove all the fat that rises to the surface. Reduce the remaining liquid by 3/4 constantly removing the fat and impurities that rise to the surface. Taste the sauce and season accordingly. Set aside.

For the purée: Boil the chopped cauliflower with the milk till tender. Strain and leave to dry but do not let go cold. Liquidise to a fine purée. Season, add butter and set aside.

For the Florets: Add all the dry ingredients together. Add enough water to form a smooth batter with the consistency of custard. Place Florets into batter, fully coat and deep fry till crispy. Set aside.

To assemble: In a hot non-stick pan cook the scallops to a nice caramelised golden brown on one side. Turn them over off the heat and set aside. Place 3 portions of the hot seasoned cauliflower purée down the centre of the plate. Place 2 crispy florets between the portions. Place 3 scallops caramelised side upwards on each portion. Add the tomato cubes and small pinch of chopped herbs to the sauce and spoon around, giving 5 cubes per serving. Arrange mixed salad over the top of the scallops and serve.

Seared Scallops with Cauliflower Puree, Florets and a Chicken and Herb Sauce

Chef Profile

Describe your style of cooking
Homemade and Wholesome. We take great care in preparing and cooking our food.

Training and background
Left college and have worked as a Chef for 25 years in family owned pubs/restaurants.

What's the best advice you have ever been given?
To stay as an independent. Running your own restaurant requires you to always aim higher and become better as your diners are important to you. You want them to come back!

What food would you say is good value for money?
In our restaurant, definitely steak and kidney pudding - the fish and chips are pretty good too!

What is your favourite comfort food?
Definitely Lamb Chops.

Which chef do you admire most?
Rick Stein.

Do you think Britain's culinary reputation has advanced in recent years?
Yes, this I believe is down to the interest the public now have in what's put in front of them. More programmes on the TV has created more food critics, which ensures what comes out of the kitchen ticks most of the boxes.

The White Hart, Grafton Regis

Alan Drake M.B.I.I.

In The Kitchen

Ingredients - Serves 6-8

- 1 Large Onion
- 4 Cloves of Garlic
- 10 Ripe Tomatoes
- 2 Large Carrots
- 2 Sticks of Celery
- 1 tbsp Tomato Puree
- Small Bunch of Fresh Rosemary
- 4 tbsp Good Olive Oil
- 3 tbsp Plain Flour
- 2 pints Vegetable or Chicken Stock
- As much Double Cream as your hips will allow!

Method

1. Peel the garlic and chop.
2. Peel the onion and chop into small pieces.
3. Roughly chop the tomatoes.
4. Put a large thick bottomed pan onto the hob. Put in the olive oil and onions, cook until the onions are soft and starting to brown, add salt and pepper.
5. Add chopped tomatoes, carrot, celery and tomato puree and stir well.
6. Add flour and stir well for 3-4 mins.
7. Keep the heat quite high and gradually stir in the vegetable stock, keep stirring well.
8. Add the fresh rosemary, pop a lid on and simmer for 10 mins.
9. Carefully remove the rosemary and blend in a food processor or with a hand blender.
10. At this stage add a little drop of vinegar and a teaspoon of sugar.

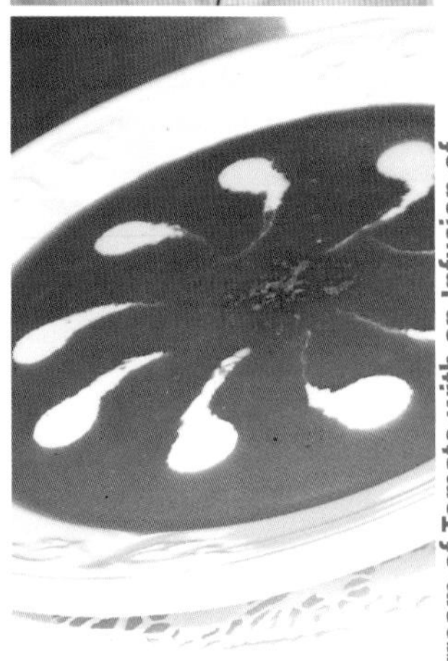

Crream of Tomato with an Infusion of Homegrown Rosemary

ORDER THE FOODIE GUIDE FOR A FRIEND

'The Perfect Gift'

- **Step 1** Fill in the name and address details of the recipient.
- **Step 2** Write your personal message (this tear out section will be enclosed with the guide).
- **Step 3** Fill in your name and address details on reverse of message section.
- **Step 4** Return **both** completed sections to us with a cheque for £6 per book (p&p FREE).

N.B. Guides are despatched via Royal Mail. We will send you a receipt once despatched.

Please make cheques payable to The Foodie Square Guide Ltd and post (no need for a stamp) to:-
Freepost RSKB-RHRA-RZBT, The Foodie Square Guide Ltd, 373 Welford Road, Northampton NN2 8PT.

Step 1

ill in the name
nd address
letails of the
ecipient.

Please post to:

Name ....

Address ....

....

....

Postcode ....

Write your message below and then **fill in your details on the reverse** -
we will do the rest...

Step 2

Vrite your
ersonal message
this tear out section
vill be enclosed with
he guide).

Your message:

....

....

....

....

....

....

THE FOODIE GUIDE has been sent to you from:

Name

Address

Postcode

Tel

Email

Step 3

Fill in **your** name and address details.

Step 4

Return both sectio
with your cheque t
Freepost RSKB-RHRA-RZBT,
The Foodie Square Guide Ltd,
373 Welford Road,
Northampton,
NN2 8PT.

BEAUTIFULLY

HOMES
& GARDENS

BECOME ONE

THE DAY SPA
WHITTLEBURY HALL

Pure indulgence...

Hotel & Spa Breaks
from £59pp*

Escape with our purely indulgent offers

Enjoy a rejuvenating escape with friends and family in our **award-winning facilities** and take time out to refresh in our luxurious spa

To find out more call us today on **0845 400 0002 (Quote FOODIE)** or visit **www.whittleburyhall.co.uk/indulgence**

*Terms & Conditions apply. Subject to availability. See website for full details.

little KNOX.

Little Knox carry out mobile car body repairs in the Milton Keynes area, seven days a week, repairing small to medium damage at your convenience, either at your home or place of work.

A family run business established in 2003, we provide a first class professional service to private individuals, trade customers and car fleet managers.

From little scuffs to more extensive damage we will restore your vehicle to its original condition, often at a price less than your insurance excess.

Quotes are free, so give us a call.

- Scratches
- Minor dents
- Bumper scuffs
- Alloy wheels
- Windscreen chips
- Stone chips
- Interior trim
- Mobile service 7 days a week
- Free quotations

'Safe in our hands'

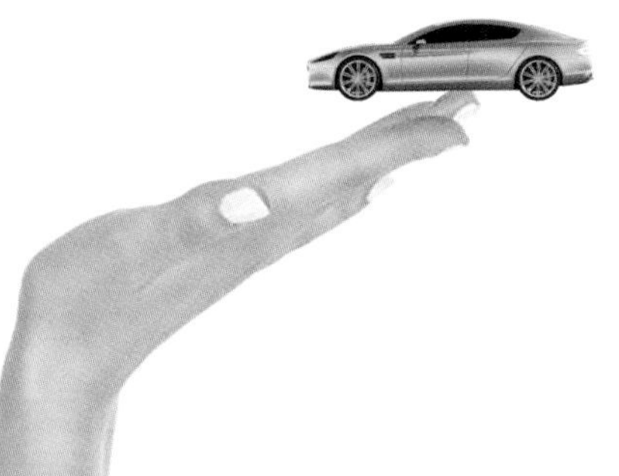

14 North Crawley Road, Newport Pagnell, Bucks, MK16 9FE

● 01908 615356 ● 078 78 28 58 12 ● info@littleknox.co.uk ● www.littleknox.co.uk

mandala

Health and Beauty Limited

Mandala Health & Beauty is located in the heart of the market town of Olney, just off the Market Square in a quiet picturesque courtyard. Established since November 2000 as a small privately run beauty salon we have been constantly expanding and improving the range of treatments on offer as well as increasing the number of treatment rooms available.

Mandala is a Sanskrit word that means 'whole world' or 'healing circle'. From the Native American and Tibetan sand paintings, the Gothic rose windows and Hindu yantras, mandalas are used as symbols for meditation, protection and healing and this name was chosen as it reflects the philosophy of the business.

Mandala Health & Beauty offers the ideal opportunity for people, men and women alike, to escape from the stresses and strains of today's lifestyles and to enjoy one of the many treatments offered.

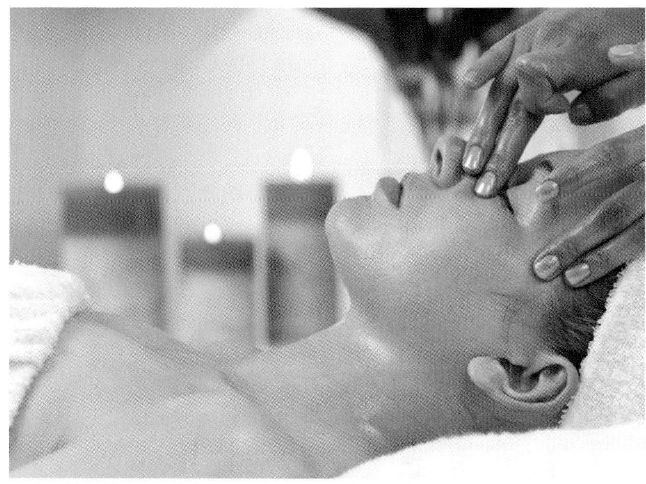

Our therapist's unique skills, genuine passion for client care, personal understanding of the needs of each individual along with a wide choice of beauty and holistic treatments are important to us in order to ensure that you are left feeling refreshed, relaxed and ready to step back into your world again.

Come and experience the time for you and let us treat you to what your mind, body or soul deserves.

We have regular promotions and can also cater for group bookings and home visits for weddings, baby showers, birthdays or whatever your special occasion might be.

Some of the treatments offered include; ESPA facials, spray tans, massages, OPI manicures and pedicures, waxing, nail extensions, eyelash extensions, reflexology, CACI non surgical face lift and many more.

Vouchers and gift packages available.

Bull Court
Olney
Bucks
MK46 4EA
Tel: 01234 714714
Email: mail@mandalabeauty.com
www.mandalabeauty.com

Opening times
Mon: 10.00am-5.00pm,
Tue-Thurs: 10.00am-9.00pm,
Fri: 10.00am-6.00pm,
Sat: 9.00am-6.00pm
Sun: Selected

ESPA

THE SPECIAL FOODIE VOUCHER.
This voucher entitles the bearer on presentation to a special offer at Galloway's Woburn.

Counterfoil

SPECIAL FOODIE Voucher

50% OFF FOOD ONLY, Friday lunchtimes
(EXCLUDES DECEMBER AND WINE TASTING LUNCHES)

at Galloway's, Woburn
Valid until 30th September 2011

Terms & Conditions on reverse.

Woburn, Beds MK17 9PZ
Tel: 01525 290496 www.gallowayswoburn.com

THE SPECIAL FOODIE VOUCHER.
This voucher entitles the bearer on presentation to a special offer at Delicatessen Estrella, Winslow.

Counterfoil

SPECIAL FOODIE Voucher

10% OFF

AT DELICATESSEN ESTRELLA
WHEN SPENDING £20 OR MORE
Valid until 30th September 2011

Terms & Conditions on reverse.

DELICATESSEN ESTRELLA

2A High Street, Winslow, Buckinghamshire MK18 3HF
Tel: 01296 712466 **www.delicatessenestrella.co.uk**

THE SPECIAL FOODIE VOUCHER.
This voucher entitles the bearer on presentation to a special offer at Olivier's Restaurant, Woburn.

Counterfoil

SPECIAL FOODIE Voucher

FREE BOTTLE OF WINE

When 2 adults dine Monday - Saturday evening from the à la carte menu only at Olivier's Restaurant

Valid until 30th September 2011

Terms & Conditions on reverse.

George St, Woburn, Bedfordshire MK17 9PX
Tel: 01525 290441 **Fax:** 01525 290432
Email: inn@woburn.co.uk
www.woburn.co.uk/inn

Terms and Conditions

- The Special Foodie Vouchers in Edition 8 of THE FOODIE GUIDE are valid until 30th September 2011.
- This voucher entitles the bearer to 50% off food, Friday lunchtimes (excluding December and Wine Tasting Lunches) at Galloway's in Woburn.
- Please bring this completed voucher to redeem this offer.
- Only one voucher may be redeemed against the final bill.
- The condition of the voucher on presentation and its acceptance is at the discretion of Galloway's.
- No photocopy or any other reproduction of the voucher will be accepted.
- This voucher may not be used in conjunction with any other offers.

IT MAY BE HELPFUL IF YOU MENTION THE USE OF THIS VOUCHER ***WHEN ORDERING*** YOUR MEAL

Name

Address

Postcode Email

If you would not like your details passed on to any third parties please tick this box ❒

Terms and Conditions

- The Special Foodie Vouchers in Edition 8 of THE FOODIE GUIDE are valid until 30th September 2011.
- This voucher entitles the bearer to 10% discount when spending £20 or more at Delicatessen Estrella, Winslow.
- Please bring this completed voucher to redeem this offer.
- Only one voucher may be redeemed per transaction.
- The condition of the voucher on presentation and its acceptance is at the discretion of Delicatessen Estrella, Winslow.
- Exchange or sale of this voucher is strictly prohibited.
- Voucher limited to single use and photocopies will not be accepted.
- This voucher may not be used in conjunction with any other offers.

Name

Address

Postcode Email

If you would not like your details passed on to any third parties please tick this box ❒

Terms and Conditions

- The Special Foodie Vouchers in Edition 8 of THE FOODIE GUIDE are valid until 30th September 2011.
- This voucher entitles the bearer to a free bottle of house selected red or white wine when 2 adults dine from the evening à la carte menu only, Monday to Saturday. Offer available for over 21's only.
- Please bring this completed voucher to redeem this offer.
- Only one voucher may be redeemed against the final bill inclusive of VAT.
- The condition of the voucher on presentation and its acceptance is at the discretion of Olivier's Restaurant at The Inn at Woburn.
- Exchange or sale of this voucher is strictly prohibited.
- Voucher limited to single use and photocopies will not be accepted.
- This voucher may not be used in conjunction with any other offers.

IT MAY BE HELPFUL IF YOU MENTION THE USE OF THIS VOUCHER ***WHEN ORDERING*** YOUR MEAL

Name

Address

Postcode Email

If you would not like your details passed on to any third parties please tick this box ❒

THE SPECIAL FOODIE VOUCHER.
This voucher entitles the bearer
on presentation to a special offer at
The Red Lion Hotel, Salford.

counterfoil

SPECIAL FOODIE Voucher

HALF PRICE BOTTLE OF WINE

AT THE RED LION HOTEL, SALFORD

when you buy a minimum of one main course

Valid until 30th September 2011

Terms & Conditions on reverse.

Salford, Milton Keynes MK17 8AZ
Tel: 01908 583117
Email: info@redlionhotel.eu
www.redlionhotel.eu

THE SPECIAL FOODIE VOUCHER.
This voucher entitles the bearer
on presentation to a special offer at
The White Hart, Grafton Regis.

counterfoil

SPECIAL FOODIE Voucher

A SOCIABLE GLASS OF WINE

for every diner on a maximum table of 4 (Tue-Thurs only)

AT THE WHITE HART, GRAFTON REGIS

Valid until 30th September 2011

Terms & Conditions on reverse.

The White Hart

Grafton Regis, Northants NN12 7SR
Tel: 01908 542123 **www.pubgraftonregis.com**

THE SPECIAL FOODIE VOUCHER.
This voucher entitles the bearer
on presentation to a special offer at
The Wollaston Inn, Wollaston.

counterfoil

SPECIAL FOODIE Voucher

FREE BOTTLE OF WINE

AT THE WOLLASTON INN

WHEN BUYING 2 MAIN COURSES

(from Restaurant Menu only)

Valid until 30th September 2011

Terms & Conditions on reverse.

The Wollaston Inn

Wollaston, Northants NN29 7QS
Tel: 01933 663161 **www.wollaston-inn.co.uk**

Terms and Conditions

- The Special Foodie Vouchers in Edition 8 of THE FOODIE GUIDE are valid until 30th September 2011.
- This voucher entitles the bearer to a half price bottle of wine when buying a minimum of one main course meal at The Red Lion Hotel, Salford.
- Please bring this completed voucher to redeem this offer.
- Only one voucher may be redeemed against the final bill inclusive of VAT.
- The condition of the voucher on presentation and its acceptance is at the discretion of The Red Lion Hotel, Salford.
- No photocopy or any other reproduction of the voucher will be accepted.
- This voucher may not be used in conjunction with any other offers.

IT MAY BE HELPFUL IF YOU MENTION THE USE OF THIS VOUCHER ***WHEN ORDERING*** YOUR MEAL

Name --
Address --
Postcode -- Email --
If you would not like your details passed on to any third parties please tick this box ❐

Terms and Conditions

- The Special Foodie Vouchers in Edition 8 of THE FOODIE GUIDE are valid until 30th September 2011.
- This voucher entitles the bearer to one free glass of house wine per diner for a maximum table of 4, when dining on Tuesday - Thursday at The White Hart, Grafton Regis.
- Please bring this completed voucher to redeem this offer.
- Only one voucher may be redeemed per table.
- The condition of the voucher on presentation and its acceptance is at the discretion of The White Hart, Grafton Regis.
- Exchange or sale of this voucher is strictly prohibited.
- Voucher limited to single use and photocopies will not be accepted.
- This voucher may not be used in conjunction with any other offers.

IT MAY BE HELPFUL IF YOU MENTION THE USE OF THIS VOUCHER ***WHEN ORDERING*** YOUR MEAL

Name --
Address --
Postcode -- Email --
If you would not like your details passed on to any third parties please tick this box ❐

Terms and Conditions

- The Special Foodie Vouchers in Edition 8 of THE FOODIE GUIDE are valid until 30th September 2011.
- This voucher entitles the bearer to a free selected bottle of wine when buying 2 main courses from the Restaurant Menu only at The Wollaston Inn.
- Please bring this completed voucher to redeem this offer.
- Only one voucher may be redeemed against the final bill.
- The condition of the voucher on presentation and its acceptance is at the discretion of The Wollaston Inn.
- Exchange or sale of this voucher is strictly prohibited.
- Voucher limited to single use and photocopies will not be accepted.
- This voucher may not be used in conjunction with any other offers.

IT MAY BE HELPFUL IF YOU MENTION THE USE OF THIS VOUCHER ***WHEN ORDERING*** YOUR MEAL

Name --
Address --
Postcode -- Email --
If you would not like your details passed on to any third parties please tick this box ❐

THE SPECIAL FOODIE VOUCHER.
This voucher entitles the bearer on presentation to a special offer at The Inspired Gourmet Cookery School.

SPECIAL FOODIE Voucher

10% OFF

ANY DAY COOKERY COURSE

Valid until 30th September 2011

Terms & Conditions on reverse.

The Old Granary
Brooklands Farm, Broughton
Buckinghamshire MK16 0HU
Tel: 01908 692918
Email: info@inspiredgourmet.co.uk
www.inspiredgourmet.co.uk

THE SPECIAL FOODIE VOUCHER.
This voucher entitles the bearer on presentation to a special offer at The Inspired Gourmet Cookery School.

SPECIAL FOODIE Voucher

A SERIES OF 6 EVENING COURSES FOR THE PRICE OF 5

Valid until 30th September 2011

Terms & Conditions on reverse.

The Old Granary
Brooklands Farm, Broughton
Buckinghamshire MK16 0HU
Tel: 01908 692918
Email: info@inspiredgourmet.co.uk
www.inspiredgourmet.co.uk

THE SPECIAL FOODIE VOUCHER.
This voucher entitles the bearer on presentation to a special offer at The Inspired Gourmet Cookery School.

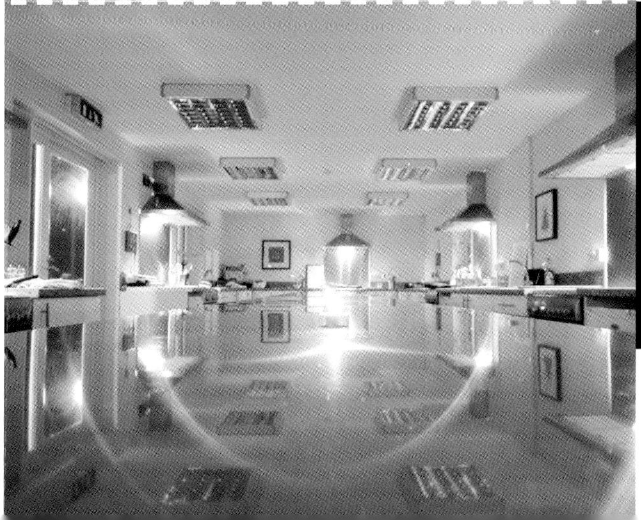

SPECIAL FOODIE Voucher

10% OFF

A COOKERY EVENT OR PARTY BOOKING

Valid until 30th September 2011

Terms & Conditions on reverse.

The Old Granary
Brooklands Farm, Broughton
Buckinghamshire MK16 0HU
Tel: 01908 692918
Email: info@inspiredgourmet.co.uk
www.inspiredgourmet.co.uk

Terms and Conditions

- The Special Foodie Vouchers in Edition 8 of THE FOODIE GUIDE are valid until 30th September 2011.
- This voucher entitles the bearer to 10% off any Day Cookery Course at The Inspired Gourmet Cookery School.
- Please bring this completed voucher to redeem this offer.
- Only one voucher may be redeemed against the final bill.
- The condition of the voucher on presentation and its acceptance is at the discretion of The Inspired Gourmet Cookery School.
- Exchange or sale of this voucher is strictly prohibited.
- Voucher limited to single use and photocopies will not be accepted.
- This voucher may not be used in conjunction with any other offers.

IT MAY BE HELPFUL IF YOU MENTION THE USE OF THIS VOUCHER ***WHEN BOOKING*** YOUR COURSE

Name

Address

Postcode Email

If you would not like your details passed on to any third parties please tick this box ❐

Terms and Conditions

- The Special Foodie Vouchers in Edition 8 of THE FOODIE GUIDE are valid until 30th September 2011.
- This voucher entitles the bearer to a series of 6 Evening Courses for the price of 5 at The Inspired Gourmet Cookery School.
- Courses must be booked and completed over the course of a single calendar year.
- Please bring this completed voucher to redeem this offer.
- Only one voucher may be redeemed against the final bill.
- The condition of the voucher on presentation and its acceptance is at the discretion of The Inspired Gourmet Cookery School.
- Exchange or sale of this voucher is strictly prohibited.
- Voucher limited to single use and photocopies will not be accepted.
- This voucher may not be used in conjunction with any other offers.

IT MAY BE HELPFUL IF YOU MENTION THE USE OF THIS VOUCHER ***WHEN BOOKING*** YOUR COURSE

Name

Address

Postcode Email

If you would not like your details passed on to any third parties please tick this box ❐

Terms and Conditions

- The Special Foodie Vouchers in Edition 8 of THE FOODIE GUIDE are valid until 30th September 2011.
- This voucher entitles the bearer to 10% off a Cookery Event or Party Booking at The Inspired Gourmet Cookery School.
- Requires a booking for a minimum of 10 people.
- Please bring this completed voucher to redeem this offer.
- Only one voucher may be redeemed against the final bill.
- The condition of the voucher on presentation and its acceptance is at the discretion of The Inspired Gourmet Cookery School.
- Exchange or sale of this voucher is strictly prohibited.
- Voucher limited to single use and photocopies will not be accepted.
- This voucher may not be used in conjunction with any other offers.

IT MAY BE HELPFUL IF YOU MENTION THE USE OF THIS VOUCHER ***WHEN BOOKING*** YOUR COURSE

Name

Address

Postcode Email

If you would not like your details passed on to any third parties please tick this box ❐

THE SPECIAL FOODIE VOUCHER.
This voucher entitles the bearer on presentation to a special offer at Beckworth Emporium.

counterfoil

SPECIAL FOODIE Voucher

FREE TEA or COFFEE

at Beckworth Emporium, when you spend over £5 per head in the restaurant.

Valid until 30th September 2011

Terms & Conditions on reverse.

Glebe Road,
Mears Ashby,
Northants NN6 0DL
Tel: 01604 812371
www.beckworthemporium.com

THE SPECIAL FOODIE VOUCHER.
This voucher entitles the bearer on presentation to a special offer at Bang & Olufsen of Milton Keynes.

counterfoil

THE NEW MASTERPIECE

SPECIAL FOODIE Voucher

10% discount

at Bang & Olufsen of Milton Keynes

(on purchases over £1000)

Valid until 30th September 2011

Terms & Conditions on reverse.

BANG & OLUFSEN

Bang & Olufsen of Milton Keynes
7 Granville Square, MK15 9JL Milton Keynes
Tel. 01908 202160, miltonkeynes@bang-olufsen.co.uk
www.bang-olufsen.com/miltonkeynes

THE SPECIAL FOODIE VOUCHER.
This voucher entitles the bearer on presentation to a special offer at Rajdhani, Central Milton Keynes.

counterfoil

SPECIAL FOODIE Voucher

25% OFF

TOTAL FOOD BILL AT RAJDHANI

(exclusions apply please see reverse)

Valid until 30th September 2011

Terms & Conditions on reverse.

Rajdhani

Central Milton Keynes MK9 3NT
Tel: 01908 392299
Fax: 01908 392541
www.rajdhanimk.com

Terms and Conditions

- The Special Foodie Vouchers in Edition 8 of THE FOODIE GUIDE are valid until 30th September 2011.
- This voucher is valid only in the Beckworth Emporium and entitles the bearer to one free tea or coffee when spending over £5 per head in the restaurant.
- The condition of the voucher on presentation and its acceptance is at the discretion of Beckworth Emporium.
- No photocopy or any other reproduction of the voucher will be accepted.
- This voucher may not be used in conjunction with any other offers.

Please visit **www.beckworthemporium.co.uk** to register for our Privilege Customer Club and benefit from exceptional offers and advanced notice of events.

Terms and Conditions

- The Special Foodie Vouchers in Edition 8 of THE FOODIE GUIDE are valid until 30th September 2011.
- Valid for purchases over £1000 including VAT in a single transaction.
- Only one voucher may be used per transaction.
- The condition of the voucher on presentation and its acceptance is at the discretion of Bang & Olufsen of Milton Keynes.
- No photocopy or any other reproduction of the voucher will be accepted.
- This voucher may not be used in conjunction with any other offers.

If you would like to be kept informed of any promotional offers from Bang & Olufsen of Milton Keynes, please fill in your name and address

Name ....

Address ....

Postcode .... Email ....

If you would not like your details passed on to any third parties please tick this box ❒

Terms and Conditions

- The Special Foodie Vouchers in Edition 8 of THE FOODIE GUIDE are valid until 30th September 2011.
- This voucher entitles the bearer to 25% off the total food bill when dining in the restaurant; excluding Buffets, all Set Meals, Thali's, Desserts and Beverages, at Rajdhani, Central Milton Keynes.
- The maximum saving is £25.
- Please bring this completed voucher to redeem this offer.
- Only one voucher may be redeemed against the final bill.
- The condition of the voucher on presentation and its acceptance is at the discretion of Rajdhani, Central Milton Keynes.
- Exchange or sale of this voucher is strictly prohibited.
- Voucher limited to single use and photocopies will not be accepted.
- This voucher may not be used in conjunction with any other offers.

IT MAY BE HELPFUL IF YOU MENTION THE USE OF THIS VOUCHER ***WHEN ORDERING*** YOUR MEAL

Name ....

Address ....

Postcode .... Email ....

If you would not like your details passed on to any third parties please tick this box ❒

THE SPECIAL FOODIE VOUCHER.
This voucher entitles the bearer on presentation to a special offer at Mandala Health and Beauty, Olney..

SPECIAL FOODIE Voucher

20% OFF

ANY TREATMENT AT MANDALA MON-FRI

Valid until 30th September 2011

Terms & Conditions on reverse.

BULL COURT
OLNEY
BUCKS MK46 4EA
TEL: 01234 714714
EMAIL: MAIL@MANDALABEAUTY.COM
WWW.MANDALABEAUTY.COM

THE SPECIAL FOODIE VOUCHER.
This voucher entitles the bearer on presentation to a special offer at The Carrington Arms, Moulsoe.

SPECIAL FOODIE Voucher

BUY 3 MAIN COURSES AND GET ONE FREE

(A LA CARTE MENU ONLY)

AT THE CARRINGTON ARMS

Valid until 30th September 2011

Terms & Conditions on reverse.

THE CARRINGTON ARMS

Moulsoe, Newport Pagnell MK16 0HB
Tel: 01908 218050 www.thecarringtonarms.co.uk

THE SPECIAL FOODIE VOUCHER.
This voucher entitles the bearer on presentation to a special offer at Galloway's, Woburn.

SPECIAL FOODIE Voucher

50% OFF FOOD ONLY, Friday lunchtimes

(EXCLUDES DECEMBER AND WINE TASTING LUNCHES)

at Galloway's, Woburn

Valid until 30th September 2011

Terms & Conditions on reverse.

Woburn, Beds MK17 9PZ
Tel: 01525 290496 www.gallowayswoburn.com

Terms and Conditions

- The Special Foodie Vouchers in Edition 8 of THE FOODIE GUIDE are valid until 30th September 2011.
- This voucher entitles the bearer to 20% off any treatment at Mandala Health & Beauty, Monday to Friday only.
- Please bring this completed voucher to redeem this offer.
- Only one voucher may be redeemed against the final bill inclusive of VAT.
- The condition of the voucher on presentation and its acceptance is at the discretion of Mandala Health & Beauty.
- No photocopy or any other reproduction of the voucher will be accepted.
- This voucher may not be used in conjunction with any other offers.

IT MAY BE HELPFUL IF YOU MENTION THE USE OF THIS VOUCHER ***WHEN BOOKING***.

Name
Address
Postcode Email
If you would not like your details passed on to any third parties please tick this box ❒

Terms and Conditions

- The Special Foodie Vouchers in Edition 8 of THE FOODIE GUIDE are valid until 30th September 2011.
- This voucher entitles the bearer to a free main course when 3 main courses are purchased from the à la carte menu at The Carrington Arms, Moulsoe.
- Only one voucher may be redeemed against the final bill.
- Please bring this completed voucher to redeem this offer.
- The condition of the voucher on presentation and its acceptance is at the discretion of The Carrington Arms.
- Exchange or sale of this voucher is strictly prohibited.
- Voucher limited to single use and photocopies will not be accepted.
- This voucher may not be used in conjunction with any other offers.

IT MAY BE HELPFUL IF YOU MENTION THE USE OF THIS VOUCHER ***WHEN ORDERING*** YOUR MEAL

Name
Address
Postcode Email
If you would not like your details passed on to any third parties please tick this box ❒

Terms and Conditions

- The Special Foodie Vouchers in Edition 8 of THE FOODIE GUIDE are valid until 30th September 2011.
- This voucher entitles the bearer to 50% off food, Friday lunchtimes (excluding December and Wine Tasting Lunches) at Galloway's in Woburn.
- Please bring this completed voucher to redeem this offer.
- Only one voucher may be redeemed against the final bill.
- The condition of the voucher on presentation and its acceptance is at the discretion of Galloway's.
- No photocopy or any other reproduction of the voucher will be accepted.
- This voucher may not be used in conjunction with any other offers.

IT MAY BE HELPFUL IF YOU MENTION THE USE OF THIS VOUCHER ***WHEN ORDERING*** YOUR MEAL

Name
Address
Postcode Email
If you would not like your details passed on to any third parties please tick this box ❒

NOMINATE
YOUR FAVOURITE RESTAURANT
AND YOU COULD
WIN A MEAL FOR TWO!

photograph courtesy of Murrays Restaurant, Whittlebury Hall

We would like to hear from you, so nominate your favourite restaurant in Beds, Bucks, Herts or Northants for THE FOODIE Award. Just fill in the details below and send the form back to us. All forms returned to us by the closing date will be entered into a draw, the lucky winner of which will receive a meal for two at one of our four award winning restaurants.*

Please only nominate ONE establishment and take into consideration the quality of food, the service, the price and the surroundings before making your choice.

I would like to nominate: ______________________________ **for THE FOODIE Award**

because ______________________________

____

Closing date for all nominations is 30th June 2011. (Winners of the current award will be published in the next edition of THE FOODIE GUIDE).

To be entered into the free draw please fill in your details below and then post back (NO STAMP REQUIRED) to:
Freepost RSKB-RHRA-RZBT, The Foodie Square Guide Ltd, 373 Welford Road, Northampton NN2 8PT.

Name: ______________________________

Address: ______________________________

______________________________ **Postcode:** ______________

Telephone: ______________________ **Email:** ______________________

*Terms and conditions apply. The meal for two is excluding drinks.

We only include restaurants in THE FOODIE GUIDE which have been recommended by *you*, so please keep sending in your comments and together we shall maintain the high standard you expect.

You can send your comments via email to: paul@thefoodieguide.co.uk
or post to: Freepost RSKB-RHRA-RZBT, The Foodie Square Guide Ltd, 373 Welford Road, Northampton NN2 8PT.

Secret Diners are a select group of Foodies who eat out regularly and notice the good (and the not so good) and would like to tell us all about it. If you give us your name and address we will send you a restaurant assessment form which you can complete whenever you eat out, then just send your results back to us - that's it, simple!!

All Secret Diners receive 3 Foodie Vouchers per assessment and are entered into a draw to win a Foodie Hamper. Closing date for the draw is 30th June 2011.

WOULD YOU LIKE TO BE A SECRET DINER? **YES** ❐ **NO** ❐

ARE YOUR NAME AND ADDRESS DETAILS OVERLEAF? **YES** ❐ **NO** ❐ (if NO please enter your details below)

Name: ______________________________

Address: ______________________________

______________________________ Postcode: ______________

Telephone: ______________________________ Email: ______________________________

extra vouchers ! FREE !

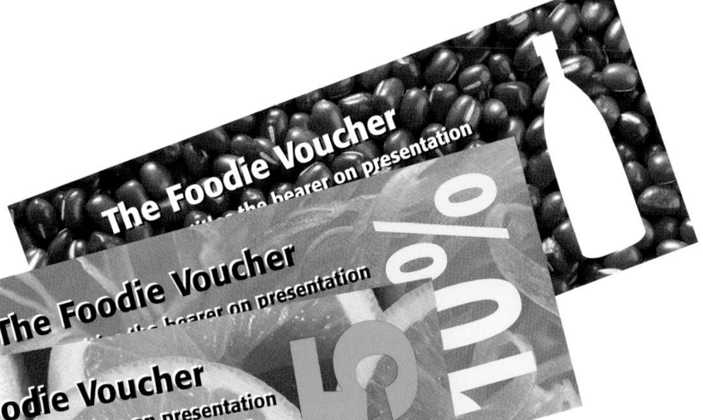

Now that you are a FOODIE GUIDE owner, we know you are serious about your food, so register your details with us and we will send you **2 extra FOODIE vouchers ABSOLUTELY FREE - or 4 vouchers if you fill in our survey on the reverse too**.

Please fill in your details below, tear this page out and send back (NO STAMP REQUIRED) to the following address:-

FREEPOST RSKB-RHRA-RZBT, The Foodie Square Guide Ltd, 373 Welford Road, Northampton NN2 8PT.

First Name: .... **Surname**: ....

Address: ....

....

.... **Postcode**: ....

Email: ....

Tel: ....

If you would like to order extra copies of THE FOODIE GUIDE at **£6** each (**Postage & Packing FREE!!!!)** please send a cheque payable to The Foodie Square Guide Ltd and indicate how many copies you would like. Thank you.

Please send me [ ] copies. I enclose a cheque for £ [ ]

THE FOODIE GUIDE Consumer Survey

1. Title: Mr / Mrs / Miss / Ms / Other (please state)
2. Name: . . . .
3. House No: . . . .
4. Postcode: . . . .
5. Email: . . . .
6. Age: Under 25 ❐ 26-35 ❐ 36-50 ❐ 50+ ❐
7. What do you find most interesting/useful about The Foodie Guide (tick all that apply)
   Restaurants ❐ Chef Profiles ❐ Recipes ❐ Fine Foods & Wines ❐ Lifestyle ❐ Vouchers ❐
8. Do you use the vouchers? Yes ❐ No ❐ (if no, go to question 11)
9. Which vouchers do you use most often? £5 ❐ 10% ❐ Bottle of wine ❐ Special ❐
10. How often do you use the vouchers
    weekly ❐ fortnightly ❐ monthly ❐ quarterly ❐ yearly ❐
11. If you don't use the vouchers is this because of the following (tick all that apply)
    Embarrassment ❐ Forgetting ❐ Not valuable enough ❐
    Restaurant doesn't accept vouchers ❐ Other (please state) ❐ . . . .
12. How often do you refer to The Foodie Guide
    weekly ❐ fortnightly ❐ monthly ❐ quarterly ❐ yearly ❐
13. Would you buy The Foodie Guide as a gift for somebody? Yes ❐ No ❐
14. What's the best feature of The Foodie Guide?
15. What's the worst feature of The Foodie Guide? . . . .
16. How would you improve The Foodie Guide? . . . .
17. Which vouchers would you like for filling in this survey?
    £5 ❐ 10% ❐ Bottle of wine ❐
18. Any other feedback . . . .
    . . . .